A1   £3.50
5/24 M

THE
LEONARDO
QUESTION

Caroline Wiseman

Strawberry

Strawberry Art Press

ISBN 978-0-9553194-2-6

www.theleonardoquestion.com
www.carolinewiseman.com
caroline@carolinewiseman.com

Contents

Nel mezzo del cammin di nostra vita
mi ritrovai per una selva oscura,
che la diritta via era smarrita...

In the middle of the journey of our life I found
myself in a dark wood where the straight
way was lost...

Dante, The Divine Comedy

Foreword

"Remember, the art world is a comedy," said Harold Rosenberg who wrote for the *New Yorker* during the 1960s and 70s.

Perhaps it is. It seems that every character in *The Leonardo Question* has come out of *Alice in Wonderland*. Except that everyone is real, except Paul Goldfarb.

Often, I have combined scenes and dialogues; but everything everyone does or says actually happened, or might have happened.

The Divine Comedy. Yes, I am in the middle of the journey of my life in a dark wood. Perplexed, like so many millions of others by modern art, I set out to find my own 'Virgil', our guide.

For the men in my life

Prologue

The Tuscan sun is burning my fair skin. I walk as quickly as I can from the café on the corner into the street with the tall Florentine houses on either side. It is hot and noisy – with little Fiats rushing past and impatiently honking their horns. I push my hair back up in its clip.

Suddenly, a motorbike screeches past me, but I keep my nerve and continue walking straight ahead. I have to find the answer. *I know that the answer will affect millions of people all over the world. The answer is worth millions of pounds.* This is the house. I check that I am not being watched. I walk up to the huge old door. I place my hand on the large round door handle.

The door opens...

Inside is as cold as outside is hot. I slip in and close the heavy door behind me. I need to adjust my eyes to the semi-darkness of the hall. The stairs creak as I ascend.

On the landing is another door. I open it.

Act I

The Players

Leonardo da Vinci (1452-1519) was born near Florence, Italy; the illegitimate son of a local notary. He was educated in the studio of the painter Verocchio. Leonardo da Vinci is described as the archetypal Renaissance man, being a scientist, mathematician, engineer, inventor, anatomist, architect, botanist, as well as painter. He had many patrons including the Borgia and the Medici families and the King of France.

Salai was born c. 1490 in Tuscany, Italy. He was the pupil and servant to Leonardo da Vinci and possibly his adopted son. It is thought that he inherited *Mona Lisa* (often called *La Giaconda*) in Leonardo's will.

Leonardo da Vinci's studio,
Florence c. 1507

Sunlight flooded in through the large window in front of me. Now, I needed to adjust my eyes to the light and I looked around. Perhaps it was an artist's studio because everywhere was covered in papers, brushes, pens, canvases, and there were several easels.

Standing before me was a tall, slender man with a handsome face and a long, white beard, rather like Moses. He smiled and bowed his head. He introduced himself: Leonardo da Vinci, and also a youth, Salai, who was lounging to one side.

He invited me to look around. On every table top were objects – skulls, bones, skeletons, microscopes, books, pages of strange writing, drawings, paintings. The drawings were exquisite, often drawn in red ochre.

Many were of the young man, Salai, who was beautiful with chiselled features and, like Leonardo, had the blond hair typical of some Tuscans. Still more were of grisly old men. Then there were drawings of babies in the womb, and several technical drawings of aeroplanes and other mechanical contraptions. There too on his desk was the famous drawing of Vitruvius with the markings all laid out precisely according to the rules of perspective.

I was in the studio of the most famous genius of the Renaissance.

I explained who I was and how I had come to be in his studio in early 16th century Florence. "Illustrissimo Maestro Leonardo, I have come here to see you to seek your advice on a very important question," I said.

He motioned for me to sit down. "I live in the early 21st century, almost exactly 500 years from now," I said. "And my question is about art. You are the only person I can ask."

He looked at me quizzically. "Yes you, Maestro Leonardo, you because you are the Renaissance man. You can look at the situation objectively."

I looked into his serene face with its large blue eyes, "I know how passionate you are about art. I am too. And so are millions of people around the world," I said. "That is why I have come to you now."

"Painting is the noblest calling open to mankind," he said softly.

"You, and Raphael and Michelangelo – your influence has continued right through the centuries through Baroque, classicism, romanticism and impressionism.

"Then came modernism and now post-modernism. And that is where we are now and we need to think about where to go from here. The question is, Maestro Leonardo, where can art go from here and very specifically who will be the next modern master?

"Maestro Leonardo," I continued, "will you be our guide, our Virgil? And may I humbly be your Dante?"

I waited for a response and then I added, "I will recount to you what's been happening in the modern art world, and ask for your guidance and wisdom."

Then I added: "In a sense, Maestro Leonardo, the story of the art world is like a divine comedy, and perhaps the aim is to find Paradise."[1]

He laughed, and called to Salai, who was parading around in an elaborate pair of shoes, and asked him to bring us some refreshments. (Leonardo later told me that he had bought twenty four pairs of shoes for Salai that year.)

Suddenly, Leonardo pulled the cloth off a canvas that was standing on an easel beside his desk.

"Mona Lisa!" I instinctively spoke in hushed tones. "Her enigmatic smile. The mistiness of her mouth and her eyes!"

"*Sfumato*," Leonardo said.

Leonardo told me how he used many layers of paint from dark to light to create these mysterious effects. "She is luminous, mysterious, as if she possesses the magical power of ancient creation," I said.

"Shadows and lights are the most certain means by which the shape of anybody comes to be known," he said looking at the portrait, lovingly.

I stood in front of her: "She is profoundly moving, she seems to express an inner life. The way the light…"

"Bathing objects in light is merging them in the infinite," he said, and offered me a mug of grape juice.

"You understand the laws of nature, and well, I know that you understand how nature works through your…", (I didn't like to say 'dissections', as I knew this was a touchy subject with the townspeople of Florence and that he had done up to thirty complete autopsies secretly at night.)

"You, you are the first artist to paint nature as it really is."

"*Una cosa mentale.*"

"A mental act. Yes, art is a mental act." We were somehow understanding each other very well, although I came to realise that Salai could not understand anything we were saying at all.

"I can't get over seeing the Mona Lisa; she is the single most influential painting of all time. As you know, Michelangelo and Raphael have both copied so many revolutionary things about her – her *sfumato*, her pose, the composition, the perspective."

Leonardo was listening attentively to me.

"The Mona Lisa has influenced artists through the centuries," I continued. "We have had many masters, none as great as you, of course... Caravaggio, Poussin, Velasquez, Ingres…"

Leonardo was eager to know how they painted. I explained, giving as much detail as I knew, and then said: "But then, unfortunately many forgot about the profound mystery, and the starting from scratch as you were describing. They merely copied technique and became academy painters."

"The painter produces pictures of small merit if he takes for his standard the pictures of others," Leonardo said, and then he added: "The Romans imitated each other and their art constantly declined from age to age."

"Yes," I replied. "And, I think that might be what is happening now."

Salai was alternating between bouts of rather bad drawing, strumming notes on a lute and walking round the studio in his heels vying for Leonardo's attention.

But Leonardo was absorbed in our conversation.

"Maestro Leonardo, your painting, the Mona Lisa, is also the most famous painting of all time in the whole world." He looked at me.

"At first she hung quietly in the Louvre. Then she was chosen by a French Emperor called Napoleon Bonaparte to hang in his bedroom. She began to be referred to by writers such as Proust and Freud.

"She was stolen from the Louvre in 1911 and made headlines in France for weeks. She became world famous when she was taken on exhibition to New York and to Japan," (Leonardo wanted to know where these places were so I gave him a quick geography lesson).

"Maestro Leonardo, your Mona Lisa, as well as being famous, and very important for the history of traditional art, is also so important for the history of modern art." He was inspecting his long thin fingers, but then he looked at me, wanting me to explain more.

So I continued: "There are three painters who have been the most influential to the art of the 20th century and now the 21st century. Yes, you, Maestro Leonardo; a Spaniard, Pablo Picasso, and a Frenchman, Marcel Duchamp." Leonardo was sitting with his back to the large window. He was elegant in a simple shirt and leggings, but Salai, his servant, pupil, maybe adopted son, lover even, I did not know, was dressed in a much finer jacket and breeches.

"Now, the story of modern art; I would like to tell it to you and to an imaginary audience as a play. And I would like to tell it to you through the important moments which have shaped the course of modern art, over more, or less exactly one century. And the key players will re-enact those important moments using their actual words.

"It will be as uncomplicated as possible," I continued. "Not because you need it simplified, Maestro Leonardo, but so that everyone will understand and dare to have an informed opinion about where modern art can go from here, and the confidence to speak it."

Leonardo put a new canvas on an easel. He told me to take off my earrings, my wedding ring, my watch (by which he was fascinated), and my jersey, leaving on just my black T shirt and jeans.

I had drunk too much liquid. I could not ask my exalted host, so I turned to Salai, who had been lounging on a day bed.[2] Through motions and gestures he got the point. I feared an earth pit in the garden, but instead he opened a door off the studio and there was a gleaming white toilet. I dashed in gratefully, not thinking about the incongruity of it.

A couple of minutes later, having also reapplied my lipstick, I reappeared. (Unbeknown to me, while I was in there and while Leonardo must also have been out of the room, Salai had stolen my iPod from my handbag.)

Leonardo asked to me to sit on a chair before him. He studied me intently. Then he dipped his brush in his paint...

Notes

[1]Leonardo told me this story: He had been in Florence one day when he saw a group of townspeople discussing Dante. They begged him to explain some verses of *The Divine Comedy*. Just then Michelangelo appeared. "Michelangelo will explain the verses you are talking about," Leonardo had said. But Michelangelo apparently replied, "You, who make the model of a bronze horse and could not even cast it." Michelangelo left, leaving poor Leonardo feeling very embarrassed.

[2]Fans of the Da Vinci code will be disappointed that I did not find out whether Leonardo, as Grand Master of the Priory of Sion, had orgies on the bed. Leonardo had been acquitted of sodomy several years earlier, but naturally that did not affect my good opinion of him.

Leonardo had started to paint me now, so I began my story.

Act II

The Players

Pablo Picasso (1881-1973) was born in Spain and came to live in Paris in 1900. He is possibly the most renowned artist of the 20th century.

Gertrude Stein (1874-1946) was an American writer who lived in Paris and devoted her life to the development of modern art and literature. She held a weekly salon which she shared firstly with her brother, the collector Leo Stein, and later with Alice B. Toklas.

Alice B. Toklas (1877-1967) was born in California and came to live in Paris in 1907. Together with Gertrude Stein she hosted a salon whose members included Picasso and Matisse as well as expatriate American writers. She and Gertrude were a couple until Gertrude's death.

Daniel Henry Kahnweiler (1884-1979) was a German art historian, collector and prominent art dealer. After initial training as a stockbroker, Kahnweiler moved to Paris and came to the forefront of the avant-garde artistic scene when he opened his art gallery in 1907.

Pablo Picasso's studio, Paris c. 1907

Modern art began in Paris, in the large, chaotically clustered studio in the Bateau Lavoir where a young Spanish artist called Pablo Picasso lived with his mistress and model, Fernande Olivier. The year was 1907. It was 11 o'clock in the morning and there was loud knocking on the door.

"Pablo, Pablo. It is me, Gertrude. With my friend Alice for you to meet." The young lovers lay in bed in the studio beneath a window which had the shutters still closed.

The beautiful girl got up and ran out of the room. The man was small and stocky with jet black hair and large black eyes. He pulled on a pair of trousers and went to open the door, barefoot. Two women were standing there. One, the one with the booming voice, was imposing, not tall but broad and masculine; the other was small and birdlike.

"Pablo, meet Alice B Toklas. Alice and I are in love. It was love at first sight." She spoke in French with an American accent.

"*Enchanté, Mademoiselle*," Picasso replied, in his own more subdued Spanish accent.

Gertrude strode across the large studio which, as Picasso had now opened the shutters, was in bright sunlight. Now they could see the shambolic mess of old junk, canvases, newspapers, bottles, stones, skulls, bones, peeling wallpaper, all beneath layers of dust.

"What a horrible mess!" Gertrude screamed looking at the very large canvas on an easel. "That's what Leo called it. He's been laughing till his sides burst."

"Your brother has been a good and loyal patron to me," Picasso said.

"Now it seems I will have to take over the avant-garde role," said Gertrude. "I was the first to buy Matisse when I saw his *La Femme au Chapeau* at the Salon and everyone was laughing at it. Leo and I bought it. And now we buy Picasso too. Now I am the one with the eye."

Picasso turned his eyes on to Alice who was looking intently at the huge painting, not knowing what to say.

"Watch his Andalusian *miranda fuerte*, Alice, his gaze that undresses you. Don't be alone with him. He will want to conquer, seduce and possess you with his eyes," said Gertrude.

Gertrude was looking at the canvas again now. "It is enormous. It is strange with light and dark colours. It is frightening, something painful and beautiful there and oppressive but imprisoned."

"*C'est bien fort*," said Picasso absent-mindedly, as he was looking at Alice.

"Pablo, there are five whores in it and each of them looks like Fernande, and look, this one is Fernande squatting on the bidet over there," said Gertrude.

Picasso turned now to look at the enormous canvas. "I want to comment on the animal nature of women. But my characters are imaginary."

"So you are not representing nature?" asked Alice.

"No, I don't work after nature, but before nature and with her."

"Pablo, you are tearing up the rule-book, art rules we've had since the Renaissance," said Gertrude.

"*Bien.* A painting should be ballsy," said Picasso. "Leonardo was near the truth when he said painting is something that takes place in the mind, but he is only half way there. Cézanne came closer when he said painting is something you do with your balls. I'm inclined to think it's a question of both Leonardo and Cézanne."

Picasso was enjoying making Alice blush.

"I can see negro influence," said Gertrude, "Matisse introduced you to it, didn't he?"

"No, not at all," insisted Picasso.[1]

"And Iberian influence," continued Gertrude. "Those Iberian heads I saw last time I came here, they weren't the two that were stolen from the Louvre were they? Where are they now?"

"I know nothing. No negro influence. No Iberian influence. Nothing from Matisse."

"Well, Henri is coming on Saturday to my salon. This painting of yours will be the talk of the evening. Henri will be put out. It will compete with his new painting *Bonheur de Vivre*. He won't want you to meet his new Russian patron,

Sergei Shchukin. But, actually," for the first time Gertrude sounded quite sweet, "knowing Matisse's generosity I expect he will bring Shchukin here to see this new painting of yours. Shchukin's patronage will help you alot.[2] Now where is La Belle Fernande?"

Gertrude, in her long shapeless dress and sandals strode off to let Fernande know that her pupil Alice was ready for her French lesson. Immediately Picasso was alone with Alice, he took hold of her hand, but then quickly let go of it again when Gertrude strode back in.

"Picasso squeezed my hand," Alice told Gertrude. Gertrude dropped her hand bag. "Ah! And what else?"

"Nothing," said Alice.

"If, when he squeezed your hand an emotion entered his imagination, that might be the beginning of a permanent feeling. It might even be love."

Alice went pale. "I must go for my French lesson," she said and ran off to find Fernande.

There was a knock on the door.

"Ah, Kahnweiler," said Picasso. "*Bonjour, Monsieur.* Do you know Mademoiselle Stein?"

Daniel Henry Kahnweiler was a handsome young

German who had decided to deal in paintings by the most progressive young artists rather than enter his family's banking business.

"Come and look at my new painting, *Les Demoiselles d'Avignon*," said Picasso.

Kahnweiler looked at the huge canvas. "*Insuccés.* Unsuccessful. A failure. Monstrous. Horrible. But... captivating. I am overwhelmed."[3]

"*Eh bien*," said Picasso. "My friend Braque says it looks like someone drinking gasoline and spitting it out."

"Pablo, you are out to shock, if not appal," said Gertrude.

"I want to understand and penetrate the secrets of art which I want to make look new and fresh."

"Pablo," Gertrude's voice was loud and strident, "you are a revolutionary. This is the moment of liberation — perspective is abolished."

"Exactitude is not truth. To sum up the great emotions, that is the purpose of art," said Picasso.

"Yes," said Kahnweiler, " and this painting, this 'Cubism'[4] is a form of writing, a way of conveying emotions. Just the other day, I saw two taxi drivers laughing their heads off at an impressionist painting in a gallery window. Painting makes us see the world anew and when a painter like Picasso here invents new signs, new ways of doing this, there arises a conflict, and this is what causes the laughter, the outrage."

Kahnweiler continued, "Vollard was telling me how you, Picasso, came to his gallery without appointment and he had a show for you which was completely unsuccessful, and he sold no paintings at all."

Picasso was not interested in hearing this and was looking round to see where Alice was.

"And then," Kahnweiler continued, "he was saying how he was putting names into a hat with a group of clients to guess who will be the next great master. Cézanne won, and his client bought thirty of them."

"Cézanne was my one and only master," said Picasso. "It is not what an artist does, but what he is. Cézanne has anxiety, and it is this anxiety which compels an artist to set his sights ever higher so that each brushstroke constitutes a little victory snatched from the maw of defeat."

"You have such natural artistic skills, Pablo," said Gertrude.

"The greater an artist's ability," Picasso said, "the more

fiercely he has to combat facility and virtuosity by making things as difficult as possible for himself – without, of course, making it look difficult."

"Yes, and this, here, this is the painting which will liberate a creative energy," said Kahnweiler, "which will transform the art of the whole world and will make you, Picasso, the most influential artist of our time."

"I will be the Mahdi of modern art, not Matisse."

Kahnweiler negotiated with Picasso to buy a small gouache study of the big painting, and took his leave.

Gertrude meanwhile, was looking round for Alice and started singing: "Where is my delicious dish, my little wife? A rose is a rose is a rose is a rose is a rose."

Gertrude walked back in with Alice, "Pablo, you know your misogynistic verso has a recto which is compassionate, generous and loving."

"Mademoiselle Toklas, how is your French now?" asked Picasso ignoring Gertrude.

"We talked about the names of dogs."

"Thank you for taking Fernande off my hands." And then to himself he said, "Fernande is no longer a goddess, but a door-mat."

"These shoes, they can't all be Fernande's!" cried Gertrude. "All this rubbish, skulls, bones, and what are these? Pablo! The two Iberian heads!

"You said no Iberian influence. Once you have used them, taken their magic, you discard them. Like you do with everything, like you have done with poor Fernande. These two heads are very like the two stolen from the Louvre. You wouldn't have anything to do with that would you, Pablo? If a painting like the Mona Lisa ever got stolen from the Louvre they might just suspect you!"[5]

* * *

Leonardo put down his brush. I got up and walked over to the window and looked out at the Florentine buildings close by and then further afield to the Tuscan landscape so familiar to me from Leonardo's paintings.

Leonardo was obviously intrigued by my story. I could see that he identified with the artist in Picasso. He told me about the 'burning desire' he had had since childhood to learn about everything and that this took him to the threshold of the 'impossible'. He reminded me that "a pupil should always excel his master," in other words, he had nothing but respect for Picasso for taking art on to the next step.

He totally understood the rivalry between Matisse and Picasso and confided in me about the rivalry between himself, Michelangelo and Raphael.

* * *

Notes

[1]Matisse had introduced Picasso to African art, but Picasso never admitted it.

[2]Matisse did take Shchukin to Picasso's studio to see *Les Demoiselles d'Avignon* in the autumn of 1908. Initially appalled, Shchukin became one of Picasso's few dependable collectors.

[3]Kahnweiler said this at the time, but later said he was bowled over with admiration.

[4]The art movement was not called Cubism until later.

[5]Four years later *Mona Lisa* was stolen from the Louvre, and Picasso was interviewed as a suspect.

We took our places and I began the next instalment
in the story of modern art

Act III

The Players

Peggy Guggenheim (1898-1979) was a member of the wealthy American Guggenheim family. However, her father died on the Titanic, when she was fourteen years old, having lost part of his inheritance. Peggy went to live in Paris in her early twenties and married her first husband. After their divorce she moved to London and in 1938 opened the Guggenheim Jeune Gallery. In 1939 Peggy planned to open a museum of modern art in London with her friend Herbert Read as its director, and she set about creating an important collection of modern art. In 1941 Peggy returned to her native New York with Max Ernst, her second husband. It was here that she established her gallery, Art of This Century, which she ran until 1949 when she moved to Venice. In 1980 her collection was inaugurated as the Peggy Guggenheim Collection in her Venice Palazzo and was opened to the public.

Sir Herbert Read (1893-1968) was a distinguished art historian and critic. During the 1930s he was professor of fine arts at the University of Edinburgh and editor of the *Burlington Magazine*. He was trustee of the Tate Gallery and co-founder of the Institute of Contemporary Arts. Read was a long-standing artistic mentor of Peggy Guggenheim.

Marcel Duchamp (1887-1968) was a French artist associated with Dada and Surrealist movements. He spent more and more of his time in America and his controversial ideas became increasingly influential in the New York artistic community and formed the basis of conceptualism.

Peggy Guggenheim's home, London c. 1938

"Read. Sir Herbert Read.[1] How do you do?"

"Duchamp. Marcel Duchamp. *Comment ça va?*"

The art world could hardly contain two such dissimilar men, and they were meeting for the first time this autumn afternoon in London.

"Well, Peggy's flat has some fine modern art on the walls these days. We are getting somewhere, you and I, Monsieur Duchamp, with educating Peggy into modern art. Has she asked you, like me, for a list of prospective artists for our proposed museum?" asked Herbert.

"*Mais oui, bien sûr*, Sir Herbert." Marcel Duchamp was an attractive Frenchman with an elegant bearing and he dressed stylishly in a jacket with a fur collar. He was a very old friend of Peggy's from when she lived in Paris and now he was one of Paris's most influential artists.

"But first," Herbert Read said, "I'll just have a quick look around at Peggy's new paintings," and this tall, reserved Englishman, in his bow tie, who was now an eminent art historian and critic left the elegant sitting room to look at the paintings hanging in the dining room.

But then a woman rushed in. "Where is Sir Herbert? Has he been in here? Don't let him sit on the sofa. Last time he made a mess." And she rushed out again.

The woman was Peggy Guggenheim. She was then in early middle age with her hair dyed black. She was not attractive partly because her face was dominated by a large nose.

"*Oh, là là,* well..." Duchamp was somewhat embarrassed.

Herbert Read then reappeared and as he was about to sit on the sofa, said to Duchamp, "Will you sit down, my good fellow?"

"*Non, non,* Sir Herbert, *un moment, s'il vous plaît.*"

Just then Peggy came into the room again holding a small fluffy dog, "It's alright, I've found Sir Herbert and I'm putting him outside," she said as she mockingly scolded the dog in her arms.

"*Le chien?* He is also called Sir Herbert?" asked Duchamp.

"I know it's confusing," Peggy laughed. "The staff always

say, 'Do you mean the man or the dog?' Now, darlings, have you met? Good. Tea? Good. Now you have your lists?"

The three sat down on the expensively upholstered chairs. The two men took out their lists: Herbert's from his top pocket, and Duchamp's from the small suitcase that he always carried. Peggy poured the tea.

She continued: "Poor me, I am having to tear myself away from Samuel Beckett with whom I'm terribly in love, aren't I?" Both men could see, but were too polite to mention it, that Peggy's bright red lipstick was badly applied.

"Look at that empty bed. Empty." Peggy pointed to the day-bed beneath the window overlooking the fashionable London street. "Samuel is in Paris, and because of this gallery I am supposed to live in London, aren't I? He can't make up his mind either to have me or to let me go..."

"Peggy dear, I feel we should get on with our list," said Herbert gently.

"Herbert, darling, you are just like a Prime Minister. Yes, I forgot – we have to find the next Picasso. You two are educating me in modern art. I'm very good at taking advice. I now know the difference between surrealism, cubism and abstraction. I still really prefer the old masters, Leonardo,

Michelangelo, Poussin to modern art, but Beckett says that one has to accept the art of one's day, as it is a living thing."

"May I suggest Jean Cocteau?" said Duchamp lighting his pipe.

"Cocteau? I had to go to his hotel while he lay in bed smoking opium. Then one night he invited me to dinner and sat opposite a mirror and was so fascinated he could not keep his eyes off himself. Mind you he was so beautiful, with....."

"Er, Peggy, I think we should get on." Herbert was looking at his long list of names.

"OK, sorry. Who's next?"

"Mondrian?" said Herbert.

"Piet, dear Piet. He came into my gallery and asked if I could recommend a night club. Then we danced the boogie-woogie together." said Peggy.

"Peggy, dear," Herbert looked rather odd, sitting on the sofa; he was so tall his knees reached nearly to his chest.

"He kissed me in the back of a taxi – oops, sorry, no more love life."

"Now, I'm going to suggest Henry Moore," said Herbert as he tried to assert some order. "Picasso's influence has enabled him to release the doors of his intuition so that he has gone on to establish his own method of sculpture."

"Henry, he came to the gallery like a travelling salesman, took a bronze out of his bag, and I bought it."

Duchamp was getting restless. "Do you mind if I play chess while we do this?"

"You don't mind, do you, Herbert? Marcel plays non-stop I think." Herbert was too polite to say anything about Duchamp's pipe or his chess playing.

"Er, Tanguy?" offered Duchamp, as he laid out his board and chess pieces on a side table close by.

"He was very fond of me. My ex-husband and my children wanted me to marry him but I felt I needed a father not a son. He painted these earrings I am wearing."

"Let me see them, yes, they are the most beautiful Tanguy paintings in the world," said Herbert.

"Really? Thanks, Herbert," Peggy said coquettishly.

"Brancusi?" suggested Duchamp.

"He loved me very much; my ex-husband said I should marry him to inherit his sculptures."

"Giacometti?" tried Duchamp.

"He looked like an imprisoned lion."

"Well, Leger then?" said Herbert.

"He looked like a butcher."

"Max Ernst?" said Duchamp.

Peggy's blue eyes sparkled. "Hey, I've heard he is pretty handsome and charming with the ladies."

"Well, Peggy dear, I think we should start our museum with the great master himself, Picasso," said Herbert.

"Ah yes," Peggy sat up straight in her chair. "I know that famous thing he said: 'I don't work after nature, but before nature, and with her'.

"See, I'm learning aren't I, Papa?" Peggy liked to use her nickname for her artistic mentor.

"Well, Peggy," said Herbert, "that's another of Picasso's gnomic utterances. But yes, Picasso's cubism was a watershed between interpreting the visual world as it is and art that exists independently as the pure fruit of the imagination."

"I guess Picasso was revolutionary, right?"

"Certainly. With cubism he rejected aesthetic notions going right back to the Renaissance," said Herbert.

With a jolt, Duchamp took his pipe out of his mouth and said: "I am done with cubism − all that theory, no humour. I hate all aesthetics."

"Marcel, are you cross because you were a cubist and they

rejected that painting of yours?"[2] asked Peggy.

"That painting broke for ever the enslaving chains of naturalism."

"It certainly made you famous in New York, Marcel."

"Monsieur Duchamp," Herbert was trying to explain as much to himself as to Peggy. "You and your fellow Dadaists, you loathe the traditional idea of art imitating nature?"

"*Oui, eh bien*," Duchamp's English was shaky. "Now that Picasso's cubism has freed art from dependence on nature, on the exterior world, why should art be limited to visual things?

"Art can be an idea, the idea of an artist – *moi*!" and he reached behind him and pulled out a large white porcelain object and pushed it in front of him so that the three could see it.

"*Voilà!*"

"Hang on, old chap." Herbert was horrified. "Picasso being revolutionary is one thing; now it looks like you're even more of a revolutionary, a complete iconoclast, if I may say so."

"I am interested in ideas, not in merely visual products," said Duchamp.

"Marcel, it's a urinal that men use in public washrooms!" exclaimed Peggy. "It's rather.. er.. beautiful, isn't it?"

"*Non. Pas joli.* Everyone, including Picasso, they are just interested in retinal art – the eye, they glorify craft – making things."

"You and your brothers are actually superb draftsmen," said Peggy.

"I have, as you say, unlearned to draw. Whether I have done it with my hands or not, I chose it. Art is not painting reality. It is reality itself. Like this urinal. My readymade. It is art because I, the artist, decide it is art. Art and life, they are one and the same."

"Monsieur Duchamp." Herbert was trying to put Duchamp's ideas into art historical perspective. "I know that your thoughts on art as a mental act have been linked to those of Leonardo da Vinci, that most mysterious of geniuses. Both of you, dedicated to the limitless concept of art as an idea."

"Ah, Leonardo da Vinci! *Voici!*" Duchamp opened his little suitcase and took out a postcard of the Mona Lisa onto which had been painted a moustache and a beard.

"Marcel, you can't do that! That's a savage attack on traditional art. Everything that is most sacred," said Peggy, genuinely shocked.

"*Oui.*"

"It's a Dada thing, isn't it." said Herbert. "Shock tactics to express your contempt for the rottenness of our civilization. What is this LHOOQ written here?"

"She has a hot ass," said Duchamp.

"You are a naughty boy, Marcel. You seem very anti- art."

"*Mais oui.* I hate beautiful art. I hate museums."

"Speaking of which, Peggy dear, you and I must go to New York to see what MoMA has. And see several collectors. I've been promised paintings we can exhibit." Herbert took his final sip of tea. "But Monsieur Duchamp, I do think you have some very original ideas but it may be as Apollinaire thought…"

"That mad poet friend of Picasso's?" Peggy asked.

"Yes, it may well be that one day your art will reconcile art and the people, but not quite yet."

"Well", said Peggy, "I'm going to buy a painting a day, including one by you, Marcel, for our museum. Now, walkies, Sir Herbert." Peggy looked round for her dog and picked up the dog lead.

"Coming, Peggy" said Herbert.

* * *

I needed to get up and stretch my legs as I was not used to being an artist's model. I walked over to Leonardo. As I had been speaking to him I had been watching his face. He never interrupted, even as I told him how Duchamp had drawn a moustache and beard on his beloved Mona Lisa.

This was obviously a very delicate thing for me to talk to Leonardo about but I could not omit it as it is key to modern art. Indeed, as I gently explained to Leonardo, it showed just how important he is to modern art. Firstly because Duchamp had based his highly influential ideas on Leonardo's assertion that art is a mental act, and secondly because it was a supreme compliment to Leonardo that Duchamp had chosen the Mona Lisa as the symbol of traditional art. Leonardo understood these points and was, I am sure, proud of his important role in the development of modern art.

There was, however, another very delicate point that I did not have the courage to bring up with Leonardo. Duchamp had questioned Leonardo's masculinity. He had suggested that the Mona Lisa was, in fact, a portrait of Leonardo himself. But I did not believe Duchamp's scurrilous interpretation. During our day together, during our breaks between painting and story telling, Leonardo told me all about Mona Lisa, who was the young and beautiful wife of a rich Florentine, Francesco del Giocondo.

Fans of the Da Vinci code will, likewise, be disappointed that I do not agree with the assertion that the Mona Lisa is Leonardo himself. Also, interestingly, when I mentioned Cocteau, who was like Leonardo supposedly a Grand Master of the Priory of Sion but several centuries later, Leonardo's face did not even flicker.

* * *

Notes
[1]Herbert Read was not knighted until 1952.
[2]*The Nude Descending a Staircase*, 1912.

We resumed our places. Leonardo looked at me intently and we began.

This act takes place in New York. Leonardo was interested to hear about the success of America, a continent which Christopher Columbus had only discovered a few years before our conversation.

Act IV

The Players

Jackson Pollock (1912-1956) grew up in California before moving to New York to study at The Art Students League. He held his first one-man exhibition at Peggy Guggenheim's gallery in New York in 1943. He became one of the most prominent members of the Abstract Expressionist group of American painters during the 1950s.

Clement Greenberg (1909-1994) After graduating from Syracuse University, Greenberg became an influential American art critic.

Peggy Guggenheim

Marcel Duchamp

Peggy Guggenheim's apartment, New York c. 1944

The war has forced Peggy Guggenheim to return to New York where she has set up her gallery/museum. Her new husband, the artist Max Ernst, has just left her.

Peggy is sitting on her bed, looking at a photograph of Max. "Max, so beautiful, such a good painter, so famous."

She kissed the photograph and tears welled in her big blue eyes. Suddenly the phone rang.

She picked up the telephone receiver, "Jackson, where are you? You're late. I've got to go to my museum." But she had to hold the 'phone away from her ear, as expletives were coming from it.

"Clement Greenberg's coming over any minute now. He's writing his piece on you. It's important, you know how respected he is. I know he's a shit. No, well, he might help you hang this painting. Yes, Marcel might help too. Just get your ass over here."

The door bell rang. Peggy slammed the phone down and opened the door to a tubby, bald man with a large nose and fleshy lips. "Clement darling, come in."

"Peggy, you're looking beautiful. Is Jackson here yet?" Clement was from the Bronx and spoke with a broad New York accent.

"On his way, I guess. But I gotta go to my museum. Do have a look around. Since I've been in New York I've kept on buying paintings and sculpture on Herbert Read's list. I know you won't approve of all of them."

"Certainly not those on Duchamp's list. Peggy, you don't always have the best taste but you have a feeling which is always alive."

She stood jauntily in front of him with her hands on her hips and said. "A good painting has originality and a bad one simply repeats the ideas of others. A purely instinctive approach makes me feel the quality. I buy things I like."

Greenberg was trying not to look at Peggy's figure, which was slim and shapely. But her dress incorporated large holes through which Greenberg could see, had he wished to, areas of Peggy's back, bottom and thighs. She wore ankle length socks and neat shoes.

Peggy hurriedly showed Greenberg the paintings on the walls, "Tanguy, Braque, Masson, my Max....most of Paris's abstract and surrealist artists have come here during the war.

Where is Jackson? Discovered him you know. He is late as always, probably drunk again last night."

"That guy is worse than me," said Greenberg looking around to see if a drink might be on offer.

"My God, Clement, we've all had such fun... including Max and me even, before he went off with that Dorothea Tanning woman, and they've been a huge influence on American painters, as you know. This new school – are we calling it Abstract Expressionism? Jackson, Motherwell, Hofmann, Rothko – I am giving them all their first shows, aren't I? No other gallery is showing them."

"You're a pioneer, Peggy." But Greenberg was looking urgently now, not at the paintings, but surreptitiously at the dining room cupboards to see if he might see a bottle of whisky.

"Jackson – he is by far my most honourable achievement," said Peggy ignoring Greenberg's efforts.

"I'd agree," said Greenberg. "He is the strongest painter of his generation and perhaps the greatest one to appear since Miró."

"When I first exhibited him he was very much under the influence of Picasso. He's also been influenced by surrealism especially by my Max, you know, Max's frottages...."

"Yes, of course and, so I gather, that idea came from Leonardo da Vinci."

Greenberg, resigned at not being offered a whisky, looked at Peggy again, and at her nose. "I read Leonardo was looking at an old wall and saw paintings revealing themselves in the patterns – all very surrealist."

"Now Jackson has moved on from all his influences and has his own personal conception," said Peggy, taking her coat, a red and black striped affair, off the hook.

"He is the new Picasso." Greenberg lit a cigarette.

"Yes, and I dedicate myself to him. We don't, you know, have a romantic relationship. He is so difficult. He drinks too much, and becomes so unpleasant, one might say, devilish."

Ding, dong.

"Jackson! Here is my Picasso –'I don't work after nature, but before nature and with her!'" Peggy laughed.

"I am nature," and Jackson Pollock marched in. He was young and handsome and bald.

"I'm late," said Peggy, "I'm just gonna powder my nose," and Peggy went into the bathroom, off the sitting room.

"Jeez quick, lady," said Pollock. "That nose, Clement, how many nose jobs has she had?[1] Oh well!" Pollock undid his trousers and began to urinate into the fireplace. "I can piss on the world."

Clement pretended not to notice. "Where does Mrs. Moneybags keep her liquor?" he was saying while, opening and closing cupboard doors.

Peggy came out of the bathroom, with bright red lipstick newly applied. "Must go, bye. Clement, don't let Jackson find the beer and don't let him go in the sitting room, there's a private party going on there.

"And Clement," Peggy continued at lightning speed, "Marcel, he's gonna help put up the painting too. I know you hate his ideas, but be nice to him because we're having an affair, but he's behaving more like a nurse than a lover."

Peggy went out, and Pollock started dragging in his huge rolled up painting.

"This fucker is nineteen feet by nine feet high! Clement, this calls for some drinks."

Greenberg had found Peggy's hidden beer and handed Pollock a bottle. "Ah, thanks, buddy," said Pollock, his head gleaming with sweat.

"Jackson, you are the greatest painter of our time – the flatness of the picture surface, abstract figures in a rhythmic dance…" Greenberg had found a bottle of whisky and was drinking from the glass he had poured himself, and smoking a cigarette.

"It's all unconscious," said Pollock, draining a bottle of beer and opening another. "When I'm in my painting I'm not aware of what I'm doing. It has a life of its own. I've got to let it come through. Then, there is pure harmony – it comes on well."

Pollock had unrolled his painting and now began to dance around it, flicking paint onto it from his brush, as he did so. Then, after a few minutes, he stopped and looked at the wall and then at the painting. "Fuck, we're not gonna get it up."

He dialled Peggy's number at the gallery, "We can't get this fucker up. It's too big!" and he slammed down the phone.

"That Peggy, always makes out she discovered me but I know when she first saw my painting she said 'dreadful isn't it?' It was that Dutch dude, Mondrian, he was the one who said he thought my painting was the most interesting in America. Then Alfred Barr agreed. I'll be in MoMA soon."

"The jury was starry eyed about you," said Clement in his most sycophantic manner.

"Yeah, Greenberg, you're right – I am the greatest painter in America. De Kooning and I had a fight in the Cedar Bar the other night – he said I was the greatest painter, and I said he was the greatest painter. Ha Ha!"

"Jackson." Clement took a huge swig from his glass, "I must go and finish my article. It'll be coming out this weekend and they'll send a photographer to your studio in Long Island."

Greenberg stubbed out his cigarette and took his hat off the peg.

"And don't let that nobody, Duchamp, cut any off the edge of your painting – the edge is most important," Greenberg said as he drained his glass and left.

Pollock dialled Peggy again: "Peggy, get that Duchamp guy over here now. And tell him to bring some big scissors. What? OK, I'll tell him to get some cigarettes for you."

The door bell rang. Marcel Duchamp, dapper as ever in his fur collar, appeared at the front door, holding a small suitcase and a large pair of scissors. "I cut off ze end of ze painting?"

"Jeez, Mr French guy, I'm hot," and Pollock began taking off all his clothes. "I'm gonna find some more beer." He opened the door to the sitting room and walked into the party which had been going on in there all morning, completely naked.

* * *

Leonardo and I got to know each other very well that day. In the breaks between our painting sessions he told me many things about himself. We spoke about the inspirational stains on the walls which anticipated surrealism four centuries later. In the stains, Leonardo told me, he saw landscapes, outlines of mountains, rivers, crags, trees, plains, valleys, and hills. He said to me: "You may also see in them battles and lively gestures, strange figures, a quick play of human faces, apparel, and a thousand other things that you will reduce to good and integrated form."

He told me they had been the inspiration for the smile on the Mona Lisa. He said he had wanted to suggest the eternal mystery, the mystery of the human spirit, the mystery of sensuality, the mystery of things barely hinted at, which fire the imagination.

Leonardo also had a fun sense of humour. He laughed at

Pollock's naughty antics, and I came to see that he enjoyed pranks himself. One day, in Rome, he told me, when he was living under the patronage of Giuliano de Medici, he entertained some visitors by blowing up the entrails of a large ram with bellows. As they were inflated, they uncannily started to float.

Notes
[1]Peggy was always conscious of her large nose, and had an unsuccessful nose operation when she was young.

It was lunchtime. Salai had been dispatched to the market and came back with some delicious cheeses, bread, and fruits. He was asked to open a bottle of white wine which Salai and I drank; but Leonardo drank modestly. "Wine gets even with the drinker," he said shaking his head.

I had just enough time to go to the gleaming white toilet to reapply my lipstick.

This was a very different world I was about to tell Leonardo about.

Act V

The Players

Andy Warhol (1928-1987) After a career as a commercial illustrator, Warhol turned to painting, documentary films and writing and set up his studio, 'The Factory', in New York during the 1960s.

Edie Sedgwick (1943-1971) was an American socialite and heiress and became one of Andy Warhol's muses. She featured in several of Warhol's short films including one entitled *The Andy Warhol Story* in which Edie satirically impersonates Warhol himself. She died of a drug overdose when she was 28.

Alfred Barr (1902-1981) was an art historian and the first Director of the Museum of Modern Art in New York. By the time he left MoMA in 1968, he had become one of the most influential figures in modern art.

Leo Castelli (1907-1999) Castelli lived in Europe and then opened his gallery in New York in 1957. He championed Pop Art and then, over the next four decades, as the most influential gallery in New York, showed the most cutting edge contemporary art.

Marcel Duchamp

Andy Warhol's, Studio, The Factory, New York c. 1965

It is a large, busy, 5th floor, midtown studio. On every wall are huge Warhol portraits. Each is made in a series, with different colour waves: Jackies, Lizes, cows, soup cans. In the centre of the studio is a stack of Campbell's soup cans, and next to it, a stack of Brillo boxes.

Lou Reed is on the record player; his songs epitomising New York in the 60s: drugs, sex and nightclubs.

A young, pretty blond girl, Edie Sedgwick, is lying collapsed on a bed in the corner. Andy Warhol is on the phone.

"Yeah, Steve. What are you wearing? What's Lou wearing? Okay. Studio 54. See you later. Hang on Steve. There's the door, Edie, can you answer the door? Look, Steve, I gotta go, bye."

Edie rolled over on the bed and moaned. So Warhol opened the door, "Hi, Marcel. Edie! Marcel Duchamp is here for his film test. How are you Marcel?"

"*Moi, je suis un respirateur,*" said Duchamp, who although

now in his 70s, still retained his elegant bearing. He walked in, wearing an overcoat with a large fur collar and carrying a small suitcase.

"Edie, what does '*respirateur*' mean?"

"Breather," Edie shouted back.

Warhol took off his sunglasses. "Gee, okay. Yeah, leave your coat there. Say, you are so famous here in New York. Do you like New York better than Paris?"

Duchamp could now see Warhol's face, which was deathly white and was crowned with a shock of silver hair.

"Monsieur Warhol, any place you stay in long enough becomes boring, even heaven, especially heaven."

"Gee, I suppose so," and they walked towards the stack of soup cans.

"These soup cans, they are interesting," said Duchamp, taking his pipe out of his pocket.

"Gee, thanks." Warhol spoke in his breathy whisper.

"If you take the Campbells soup can and repeat it 50 times, what interests me is the concept, not the retinal image – I hate retinals."

"Gee, I suppose not. I got the idea from your shows you did with that broad, Peggy Guggenheim."

"Ah, *oui*, my readymades, one of Peggy's last shows before she went to live in Venice."

"I like the way you make multiples. My guys here in the Factory make hundreds of screenprints of soup cans, Marilyns, Jackies, whatever's an icon. It's good business."

"This pop art – it is a return to the conceptual art we Dadaists made 40 years ago. Thank goodness artists have given up on abstract expressionism – too emotional."

"Yeah. Pop art comes from the outside. There's nothing beneath the surface. Edie!" Warhol saw that Edie had just got up from the bed and had gone into the toilet.

"Monsieur Greenberg, he is cross, of course. He thinks pop art is a homosexual conspiracy against the aesthetics of modernism."

"Clement Greenberg, I guess he's not such a famous critic these days."

"Now he is not influential. No critic is as influential now," said Duchamp.

He puffed on his pipe as they walked round the studio looking at the screenprints on the walls.

"They're all famous celebrities," said Warhol. "I repeat them a lot in different colours, it's good for business."

Duchamp shook his head. " Marx said, 'Everything repeats itself, the first time as tragedy, the second as a comedy. Never repeat. I have stopped making art – that is the ultimate non- repeat."

"I guess so."

Then the two men looked at a large orange screenprint of Marilyn Monroe. "She was so pretty and so famous. I like this one," said Warhol.

"Remember this, Monsieur Warhol," said Duchamp. "I, the onlooker, am as important as you the artist. You perform only one part of the creative process. I complete it. And it is I who have the last word; remember, posterity makes the masterpiece."

"Gee, I suppose so," said Warhol. Then they came to a large Warhol version of the Mona Lisa.

"Mona Lisa – Ha!" said Duchamp.

"Yeah, Mona's cool, she's so famous."

"Why should we revere art? Duchamp was puffing on his pipe. "It has no existence as truth."

"Gee, I suppose not." Warhol had lit a cigarette.

"As a drug it can be a good sedative but as a religion it's not even as good as God."

"You know I didn't think about it," said Warhol, glancing at his watch.

Then he said: "I'm gonna do a series of skulls, and then a series of dollar signs. It'll be cool."

"*Non*. Don't deal in this money society. Preserve your freedom, Monsieur Warhol. Without that no worthwhile new contribution is ever made."

"Gee, I suppose not, but I think good business is the best art," said Warhol and he got out his camera.

"This screen test. I can play chess while we do it?" asked Duchamp and opening his suitcase, took out his chess board and pieces.

"Gee, I suppose so. Edie, I need you here to do Marcel's screen test."

Warhol went into the toilet and led Edie into the studio by the hand. Duchamp could see how pretty Edie was, how slim and elfin with her blond hair cut stylishly short and her huge eyes heavily made up with black eyeliner.

He laid out his chess pieces and sat on a chair, with his pipe in one hand. Warhol put the camera in Edie's unsteady hand and she pointed it at Duchamp.

"You know," said Warhol, "I like boring things. These

screen tests are just a way of taking up time."

"You are a good filmer," said Duchamp, gazing into space, as instructed, between chess moves and looking at Edie.

"Hey, my dealer Leo Castelli's coming round soon with Alfred Barr, the Director of MoMA. They're both pretty famous. Leo's got a big collector to donate something to MoMA and Mr Barr is going to choose it."

"Well, *bien sûr*, I know Monsieur Alfred Barr very well."

"Leo's pretty clever, he's the biggest dealer in town. When I said to him: 'You killed off the second generation of abstract expressionists, all those guys who came after Pollock', he said 'but they were dead already, I just helped remove the bodies.' Ha ha, he's so funny."

"Dealers are lice on the backs of artists – useful and necessary lice, but lice all the same..."

Duchamp was interrupted by the phone.

Warhol picked it up, "Oh yeah, Liz? What right now? Oh, okay."

He put the phone back on its cradle.

"Look, Marcel, you were great, darling. We've done enough filming. So, bye now." Duchamp hardly had time to pack up his chess set and put on his coat before Warhol had pushed him out of the door.

"Edie, I got to go. Liz is in town." Warhol opened a drawer and took out a wig, identical to the one he was wearing. Edie put it on. Then Warhol powdered Edie's face and put a pair of sunglasses on her. She took off her mini skirt, leaving on her black leggings, and took off her platform shoes and put on a pair of Warhol's kinky boots.

"Now, Edie, be nice to Leo and Alfred Barr. If I get one of my pieces in the Museum of Modern Art here in New York, I'll be so famous."

Warhol went off. Then a minute later the doorbell rang. Edie, now looking exactly like Warhol, opened the door. In walked Leo Castelli and Alfred Barr.

"Andy, you know Alfred Barr, Director of MoMA?" said the very charming and urbane Leo Castelli.

"Sure. Hi," said Edie in a breathy whisper, so she sounded like Warhol.

"Mr. Warhol, how nice to meet you and thank you for showing us your work," said Alfred Barr, whose glasses and manner gave him a serious, intellectual air.

"Okay."

The two men walked all around the Factory looking at all the works of art. Edie sat on a chair staring into space.

"Alfred, you decide quality from mediocrity," said Castelli, whose voice was smooth with a hint of an Italian accent.

"But if one in ten of MoMA's choices stands the test of time, I will be doing my job," said Barr.

"Well you are the most important taste maker of modern art: Pollock, Johns, Rauschenberg, Lichtenstein, now Warhol. You are a zealot in the cause of modern art." Castelli, the master manipulator of the art world, was also a master at flattery.

"Well, we have American artists now, just as important as the European ones of thirty years ago."

"Yes, because, Alfred, you have historical perspective and lucid scholarship. You are serving modern art as well as Berenson did the old masters."

They glanced towards Edie who was still staring into space, and continued walking round.

"People think modern art is a hoax," Castelli said, "but it's now considered a social necessity. Every city has its museum. I know, I sell to them, and all their trustees are interested in the 'tradition of the new.'"

He called over to Edie: "Andy, come and show us your latest works."

"Gee, okay," said Edie, not moving.

Alfred Barr was looking very intently at every piece.

"You know, Alfred, you never stop seeing," said Castelli.

"I know how easy it is to do that. There is no finality to modern art, either in time or in character,' said Barr.

"I like to pick movements emerging, and then pick the best practitioner." said Castelli. "I've been told my clients feel I sell them the history of art in the making. Ha, ha. Andy, what would you say to that?"

"Gee, I suppose so," said Edie.

"My judgements are based to some extent on one's feelings about the personality of the artist. If there is no substance to the personality, there is probably no substance to the work."

"Gee, I suppose not," said Edie.

* * *

We had all felt refreshed after our lunch. Salai, who had had three glasses of wine and had finished up the bread and cheese went to sleep, still wearing his embroidered jacket and fancy shoes, on the day bed in the corner of the studio.

Perhaps Leonardo and Salai were used to a siesta but Leonardo hadn't suggested one. He was as alert as ever, painting steadily and asking the odd question for clarification.

Leonardo was very relaxed about Warhol's appropriation of the Mona Lisa. He could see that the Mona Lisa was not being used in any subversive way but purely as a celebration of the famous icon she had become. As he said, he himself, like so many of his contemporaries, had been obsessed with the Virgin Mary, another famous icon.

Also, for Leonardo, the idea of an artist working with a studio of pupils or assistants on a work of art, was completely natural. Salai, and sometimes other pupils, worked on some of his commissions, but he had painted the Mona Lisa himself.

He was interested in Duchamp's advice to Warhol, 'Don't deal in this money society. Preserve your freedom. Without that, no worthwhile contribution is ever made.' Leonardo told me how he had been struggling throughout his career, to preserve his freedom from his major patrons such as the Borgias and the Medicis. "The Medicis made me and the Medicis destroyed me," he said. I got the feeling that the Mona Lisa was particularly precious to him because he had painted it in the way he had wanted and, in fact, he never gave it to Mona Lisa's husband, Francesco del Giacondo, who had commissioned it.

* * *

We chatted through our short break. I had still not seen his portrait of me but that was part of the suspense of this extraordinary day.

"This part of the story takes place in Venice," I said, as we sat down again. "Peggy Guggenheim decided to settle there and found a museum for her collection of modern art." Leonardo told me a few horrific stories about artists and their patrons in Venice. Then I resumed the story.

Act V1 Scene 1

The Players

Francis Bacon (1909-1992) was born in Dublin but his authoritarian father was appalled by his homosexuality and threw him out of the house. He settled in London permanently in the 1920s and his influence as a painter grew steadily, with retrospectives in London and Paris late in his career.

Gilbert and George Gilbert Proesch (b.1943) and George Passmore (b.1942) met, as students, at St Martin's School of Art. They transformed themselves into 'living sculptures,' performing as a duo. They began to make photopieces and Tate Modern held a retrospective in 2006.

Sir Herbert Read

Peggy Guggenheim

Peggy Guggenheim's Palazzo, Venice. Early 1980s.

Sir Herbert Read, still tall and distinguished, but rather bent now, was walking along beside the Grand Canal in Venice, holding a bunch of flowers. Although he had been dead for nearly fifteen years his intellect was still as clear as a bell. Suddenly, he heard a voice screaming: "Herbert, up here."

He looked up to see a comic sight. A woman with white hair and wearing outrageously huge sunglasses was waving furiously at him.

He had arrived at Peggy Guggenheim's Palazzo.

He was taken upstairs. "Herbert darling, I hope you don't mind coming into my bedroom. I won't seduce you. It's just that we have such crowds at the Palazzo, and sometimes they even come in here! This is my famous Calder bed, he designed the bed-head."

"Interestingly abstract. Peggy dear, how are you?" said Herbert, giving her the flowers.

"Herbert, thank you. Oh, for someone dead, not bad. How are you dear Herbert?"

"Oh, I'm dead too."

"Really? You look well, considering."

Like Herbert, Peggy was very bent and walked with difficulty. She took off her sunglasses. "Do you remember my earrings, one Tanguy and one Calder? No favouritism between surrealism and abstraction!" Her laugh was just as Herbert remembered. He could see her eyes now and they were just as blue. But her face was lined and her nose was as large as ever.

"Herbert, dear, you taught me so much." Then she spoke into an intercom. "You can bring in lunch now. Sir Herbert is here. No, he's not buried in the garden. That was the dog. This is the man." She put down the phone and turned to Herbert.

"I've got six little darlings now, and we had fifty seven puppies recently."

"Goodness, Peggy," but Herbert was looking at the walls of Peggy's bedroom. "You have a good collection."

"For a poor member of the Guggenheim family, not bad, huh? Cost me forty thousand dollars; it's worth forty million dollars now, isn't it awful? Martini?"

"Thank you. A fine Pollock over there."

"I discovered him, you know. He was the next Picasso."

Peggy poured their drinks. "But Herbert, you're here for the Biennale, right?"

"Yes, as you know, I had been on the selection committee of the British Pavilion for ten Biennales, until I died in '68. Of course we showed your wonderful collection here in '48, and since then the British Council has brought over most of our important artists, like Henry Moore, Ben Nicholson, Anthony Caro, Richard Long. Each country brings over their top artists."

"I don't like art today. Bad isn't it?"

"Peggy, let's start at the beginning."

"OK, Papa, can I still call you that?"

"Of course, dear Peggy." During their long friendship Herbert had always been relieved that he had been one of the few men that Peggy had not had an affair with.

He continued: "Peggy, remember how you loved the art of the Renaissance: Leonardo, Michelangelo and the others? And Berenson was your guide."

"Oh, Berenson said to me, 'Why do you go in for all this?'" And she pointed to all her paintings. "He hated modern art but he did like Ernst and Pollock. And then darling Samuel Beckett said that I must buy art by living artists."

"So you asked Marcel Duchamp...."

"Marcel, he's dead now you know. Died the same year as you. You know we had an affair in the end, don't you? I'd secretly lusted after him since we first met in Paris when I was in my twenties."

"Yes, well, Peggy, you asked Duchamp and me to guide you in buying a collection for your museum."

"I bought a painting a day."

"Of course, we started your collection with Picasso."

"He was so rude to me. When I went to his studio he kept me waiting for ages, then he said, 'Lingerie 4th floor.'"

"But he was the most important artist this century. With *Les Desmoiselles d'Avignon* and cubism, he liberated artists all over the world. Hence we have had abstraction, then surrealism, of which your ex husband Max Ernst...."

"Dear Max, you know we made love three times in succession on our first night together. That was pretty good, wasn't it? What an exquisite body! That reminds me!"

And Peggy dashed out. Herbert sat twiddling his thumbs for a minute or so, but then took the opportunity to go to Peggy's en suite next to the bedroom.

He was back in Peggy's bedroom by the time Peggy returned, puffed out. She held up the phallus she had unscrewed from the Marino Marini sculpture in the garden. "The nuns come by this afternoon and I can't let them see this."

"Now, where were we, Peggy? Max takes us through surrealism and its element of chance, reminiscent of the wall markings which inspired Leonardo da Vinci, to the unconscious abstract expressionism of our friend Pollock."

"God, that day in my apartment in New York, when he got drunk and went into that party stark naked! Terrible, wasn't it? He's dead now. Drunk driving."

Peggy had got up and was looking out of the window. "Is that Francis Bacon down there?"

Herbert went to look. "No, I don't think so."

"Francis, up here! Come and have a drink with us."

"Oh dear," said Herbert. "I suppose he's come for the Biennale."

A minute or so later, Francis Bacon bounded in the room. Peggy slammed the door shut behind him, as she could hear the sound of several of his friends following him.

Bacon was drunk. "Got some champers darling?" he said in his upper class lisp. He had an odd round face, with skin as smooth as a baby.

"Think I'm made of money? Got some wine. How are you, Francis?"

"In a state of exhilarated despair. You two? Hello, Read, old man."

"Oh, we're both dead," said Peggy.

"So what? Life is ridiculous. Impossible. A charade."

"I've got this painting of yours," said Peggy pouring him a glass of wine. "It's the only one I've ever seen which doesn't frighten me. It looks like an ape sitting on a chest. What is it?"

The three of them looked at the painting hanging beside Peggy's bed. "One wants a thing to be as factual as possible but at the same time deeply suggestive of sensation. It's not just simple illustration," said Bacon.

"You were inspired by Picasso and by surrealism," said Herbert.

"Intuition," said Bacon, picking up his glass, "and inspired letting go. Isn't that what art's all about?" And Bacon swigged back his entire glass of wine.

But then he spat it all out all over Peggy and Herbert. "This is petrol," he screamed. He opened the door and ran out.

Peggy found a towel in her en suite, and dabbed Herbert and herself.

"Despite everything, Bacon is one of Britain's finest modernist painters," said Herbert trying to regain his composure.

"Really? I guess so. It's not him. It's this new lot. They are why I said art's bad today."

"You must blame your friend Duchamp, Peggy."

"That day he showed us that urinal, right?"

"His readymade, as he calls it. Yes, now we have conceptual art, based on Duchamp's notion that anything can be art, and that art and life are the same thing. The idea is important, not form and colour which are so important for modernism."

"Everyone's crazy about Marcel's readymades, especially that weirdo Andy Warhol."

"He's very influential. He says good business is the best art."

"That's why I say art has gone to hell. Because of the financial attitude. Painters think only of money. The boom has ruined art."

"You may be right. Warhol is promoted by the most professional of dealers, Leo Castelli. Alfred Barr…."

"Alfred….. I adored Alfred. I wanted to have an affair with him but he wouldn't."

"As Director of MoMA, Barr wanted to find American artists who could be as important as the major European artists."

"American cultural imperialism!" said Peggy. "I've got your favourite boiled fish and potatoes."

Herbert shooed a dog off one side of the bed and sat down with his plate on his lap.

"So now," said Peggy settling herself with one of her dogs on her lap while she ate her lunch, "anything can be art, including a can of shit."

"Manzoni….." but Herbert was interrupted by Peggy.

"They're just copying what the Dadaists did in the 20s, aren't they? Do you remember when someone danced in the nude with a cello?" and Peggy started laughing raucously. "There's nothing wrong with this wine, I got it on special offer. Here, Herbert I'll top up your glass."

Herbert had a tentative taste and was trying, with difficulty, to balance his plate on his knee and not let a little dog eat off his plate.

Peggy had cheered up. "And performance art. Who are those two odd men who wear suits?"

"I think you mean Gilbert and George. Performance art is all part of post-modernism."

"Post-modernism? The movement which comes after modernism which allows anything to be art? Hey, Herbert, remember Clement? He was a vile human being but he said some sensible things. I remember when he said that pop art and conceptual art, both part of post-modernism, I guess, are just a way of preferring less demanding art without being called reactionary or retarded. Ha ha.

"You know," continued Peggy, drawing closer to Herbert, "I always felt that you and I had a spiritual relationship."

"You've always been good fun," he said.

"You and I are too old for this new art," and Peggy snuggled a little closer.

"Perhaps we're not in the *zeitgeist*, as they say these days."

"The what?"

"*Zeitgeist;* it means spirit of the time."

"Really? Oh dear, and the art world is so much bigger now than in our day. And people buy art for snobbish reasons."

"But some people really like art, like you and me, Peggy."

Peggy had got up and was looking out of the window. "Everyone comes to visit me here, you know. Gore Vidal, Yoko Ono, Marlon Brando."

She was suddenly animated. "Hey, say, there are those two odd men. Hey, you two," and she was shouting out of the window now: "Gilbert, George, come up and see us."

"Peggy, I fear I must take my leave now, I have a meeting to attend," and Herbert stood up, kissed Peggy on both cheeks, and left.

Peggy was waiting for her new guests to arrive and was thinking, "Why do I collect art? Because I wanted to be loved, that's why I collected artists. I was lonely and didn't want to be alone. I wanted to feel something."

She fed Herbert's left-over fish to the little dog who was on her bed trying to lick his plate. "My dogs are all I have to love me now."

In walked the two men: George, tall and Gilbert, short. Both were wearing identical suits and were excessively polite.

They spoke in unison:

"Hello, Peggy Guggenheim.

May we have a glass of wine?"

Peggy handed them each a glass of wine and said: "Art these days, it's bad, isn't it?"

The two men replied in unison:

"Oh art, are you for the feeble of mind,

Are you for the poor-at-heart,

Art for those with no soul?"

Then, with Peggy laughing, they began their performance routine: "Underneath the arches…"

* * *

It was time for a short rest again. I was eager to see Leonardo's portrait of me, but I resisted. Instead we refilled our mugs of water and chatted.

Leonardo had laughed during much of this story. The Dada exploits in particular, made Leonardo giggle. He told me how the the King of France begged him to make something out of the ordinary, so he made "a lion that took a few steps, then opened its chest and showed it to be full of lilies."

Many times during our magical day together, I remembered the words Vasari had used to describe Leonardo: 'Occasionally heaven sends us someone who is not only human but divine, so that through his mind and the excellence of his intellect we may reach out to heaven.'

Both refreshed, Leonardo and I resumed our positions. "We are still in Venice," I said, "nearly twenty years later around the time of the Millennium."

Act VI Scene II

The Players

Matthew Barney (born 1967) is an American artist and film-maker, and his works are often ritualistic performances viewed through video. He showed at the Guggenheim, New York in 2003 and at the Peggy Guggenheim Collection, Venice in 2007.

Hans Ulrich Obrist (born 1968) is a Swiss curator and critic who co-curated Manifesta 1, the European biennial of contemporary art. He is currently Co-Director of Exhibitions at the Serpentine Gallery, London which presented a major show of Jeff Koons in 2009.

Peggy Guggenheim
Sir Herbert Read

Peggy Guggenheim's Palazzo, Venice. c. 2001

"Peggy."

"Herbert. We're both dead as dodos, but what the heck!"

"I know, but it's Venice Biennale time again, and I've brought you a present."

"A bottle of wine. You're a darling, thank you. You open it and tell me what's been happening in the art world in the years since we last had a good chat."

Both were now bent nearly double, and were wizened. Peggy was wearing a strange stripey outfit and Herbert wore his bow tie, as always.

"Well, Peggy dear, I am afraid to say that we are still in the same 'ism."

"Really? Not that same conceptualism – please!"

"The very same thing, my dear. Maybe we have progressed to neo-conceptualism now. Irony is the word."

"Is there no modernism happening, Herbert ?

Herbert had opened the bottle and Peggy poured two glasses.

"Yes, there is…"

But he was interrupted by Peggy, "Hey, this wine's good, isn't it? Now I've got your favourite boiled fish and potatoes."

Herbert's heart sank. "Delicious, thank you."

"But we must eat it quickly as a handsome man from Sotheby's or Christie's, I always muddle the two, came to visit me here to say that I am such an important client that they have hooked me up with some video link to their London auction, starts in half an hour."

Peggy and Herbert sat down on Peggy's Calder bed with their plates of food on their laps and continued chatting.

They couldn't see the window behind them, but suddenly a long thin leg with a high heeled shoe appeared. Then a slim body, which belonged to a person who seemed only to wearing an apron. The person, possibly a man, was wearing a swimming cap.

"Yes, there are some very good artists who work in the modernist tradition," continued Herbert, oblivious to the strange person who was now climbing in through the window. "But we are still officially in post-modernism, when several types of art coexist, but the dominant global art movement is definitely still conceptualism. The concept. The idea. From our friend Duchamp."

"Marcel – it's all your fault! God, he would be so bored."

The strange figure was now walking around the bedroom behind them.

"Quite so, Peggy. Now, to update you. I'll begin with an artist called Jeff Koons. He takes something kitsch, like...., if you will excuse my rudeness, that china dog of yours over there on the mantelpiece. He casts it in bronze, puts it on a plinth and presents it as high art."

"It isn't profound, is it?"

"It is supposed to challenge the way we think about life." Herbert took a sip of wine. "Oo, yes, this was a good year. And remember how shocking Picasso and Pollock seemed at first."

"Well, even so,it doesn't challenge or shock me."

"Koons had a show at the Saatchi…"

"That's the collector they call the Medici of the 20th century, isn't it?"

"He is an extremely influential art collector."

"More influential than me? How will posterity judge

me, Herbert? Medici or man eater?"

Herbert ignored this question. "Well, some young British artists..." Then Herbert saw this strange person walking stealthily around.

"Who are you, and what do you want?" Herbert stood up quickly so his plate of food fell on the floor.

"Hi, I'm Matthey Barney. I'm doing a recce for my show here in a couple of years time."

"I've read about you. Your work is grotesque, young man. Post modernism at its worst."

"It is how I construct meaning into my life," said Barney." The theme of my masochistic performances is self discipline and the closure of the sexual orifices."

"We find your uninvited entrance extremely rude, even if you are, which I don't doubt, exhibiting here at the Palazzo."

"Over my dead body," said Peggy.

Matthey Barney climbed out of the window.

"Now it's time for this auction, Herbert," said Peggy. "Now how do we turn on this video thing?"

"I've no idea, we had black and white television in my day."

A picture showing a young and handsome dark haired man came up on Peggy's huge TV screen. "There's no sound. Where's the volume?"

"What am I bid for this fine Picasso?" boomed the young man.

"Hell, too loud now. That's better."

"Do you remember that one, Peggy? You nearly bought it back in the 40s."

"What? Two and a half million pounds! That's crazy!"

"What am I bid for this fine Mondrian?"

"Piet… ah… I remember when he kissed me in…"

"We have to listen, Peggy. Now we missed that one."

"What am I bid for this fine Jackson Pollock?" said the handsome man.

"What? four point two million pounds!" screamed Peggy, "That's ridiculous! I had eighteen once. I so regret the ones I gave away."

"What am I bid for this fine Joseph Cornell?" asked the auctioneer.

"What those boxes! I used to give them away as Christmas presents! I always said they would be important, but everyone else hated them."

"I wonder if they would be worth this much today if Alfred hadn't bought Cornell for MoMA." Herbert murmured, half to himself.

The auctioneer was on to the next lot. "What am I bid for this fine Francis Bacon? Three million, three million one, three million two, three million three." Herbert suddenly jerked.

"Three million four to the elderly gentleman, in the bow tie, sitting on the bed," said the auctioneer.

"Help, Herbert, you have just bid three point four million pounds for a Francis Bacon!" screamed Peggy.

"Three million five to the bald gentleman in the front row," continued the auctioneer.

"Phew, that was lucky," said Peggy. "Now neither of us must move an inch!"

"What am I bid for this fine Wassily Kandinsky?" asked the auctioneer.

Peggy whispered to Herbert: "What was it you told me that Kandinsky said about art?"

Herbert whispered back. "He said a work of art consists of two elements. The inner and the outer. The inner is the emotion in the soul of the artist; this emotion has the capacity to evoke a similar reaction in the observer. The inner emotion must exist otherwise the art is a sham."

The auctioneer, very professionally, and in a matter of minutes, whisked through the German artists Baselitz, Kiefer and Richter, through the Italians, and then to the Americans including Schnabel and Warhol. A Koons went for four million pounds.

"Four million! What the heck! Herbert." Peggy whispered, "where is the inner emotion in Jeff Koons?"

"He is, I fear, sensationally banal but entirely relevant to the consumer age in which we live, if of course, we were not dead."

The auction had now reached the British artists: David Hockney, Patrick Heron, Howard Hodgkin, Anish Kapoor...

"Sean Scully now", said Herbert. I read that he thinks our friend Duchamp made it possible for artists to be in the game, as he describes it, as spoilers. For Scully it is the burden of making art which makes it interesting. It is both the making of it and the end product which is important."

Before Peggy had time to reply, Herbert whispered: "Now he's auctioning Frank Auerbach, a good example of

Britain's brown mud school. Considered too exclusive, that's partly why this new young YBA lot became so popular."

"What YBA lot?" Peggy whispered.

"Yes, I was interrupted earlier. A group of young British artists were impressed by the businesslike attitude of Warhol and Koons and by their use of readymades to express their ideas."

"Readymades don't need any artistic skills, do they?" said Peggy.

"These days learning a craft is deemed unnecessary, I agree with you. But, it is said that the artist needs skill which can be either making a work of art with his hands or the skill in choosing something to be a work of art."

"Really?" Peggy was enjoying watching the auctioneer.

"You need to ask your mother for some food," Herbert said to a small dog who was licking food off his plate on the floor. "Well, this collector, Saatchi became their patron, perhaps because the market had just gone into recession, and he wanted to buy cheaper younger artists."

Peggy picked up the dog. "Sweetie, come to Mummy."

Herbert continued, "Well, this current generation of artists use a lot of irony, parody and sometimes simple copying which they call 'appropriation'. They juxtapose readymades to make the viewer question his or her assumptions about life and the human condition."

"Really?" Peggy had turned the volume down but was still watching the handsome auctioneer.

"And these young artists have been described as avant garde but really I don't think they are, as they have been inside the system from the beginning. They were bought by Saatchi from their first show."

"Lots of Chinese artists, now lots of Indian ones, so many I've never heard of," said Peggy absorbed by the auction. "This Takashi Murakami seems to go for a lot, whoever he is."

"What am I bid for this fine Damien Hirst?" Peggy had turned up the volume.

"Damien Hirst is one of these YBAs, isn't he?"asked Peggy, looking round for her cigarettes.

"Yes, and he has done some interesting work but the problem is, only a few of these young artists have really powerful ideas and many of the others do works of extreme banality.

"And," he continued, "they get large amounts of

publicity, possibly because this collector, Saatchi, is in the marketing business."

"But, Herbert, wait a minute. We're still in this 'ism – conceptualism, and didn't someone say, 'hang on, this is a bit old hat?' After all, we have had every kind of crazy conceptual idea since the 60s, and even then they copied the Dadaists."

"Well, some in the American press said exactly that. Perhaps because the art world had been so criticised for being elitist in the 80s, the press were somewhat scared of being labelled reactionary; so it seems they were either silent or safely fawning."

Peggy laughed, "Best to be fawning, then you get lots of lovely invitations to all the openings all around the world. Can't risk not being invited, right?" Peggy lit a cigarette.

There was no reply from Herbert; he had gone to sleep. Peggy continued watching the handsome auctioneer, taking drags from her cigarette, until she too fell asleep.

Leonardo and I took the opportunity to have a quick break. I needed to stretch my legs and popped into the toilet for a minute.

Two hours later, Herbert awoke with a start. "Peggy, can we turn that thing off now, because I need to go to the lavatory."

Peggy woke up. While Herbert was out of the room she turned off the video link and then saw that all her dogs had licked the lunch plates clean. "Naughty little babies," she said and kissed them.

When Herbert returned, he said, "We were talking about the press. More often these days journalists do interviews with the artists...".

"You can't believe a word artists say – I know!" and Peggy laughed.

"The problem is, there is this thing called relativism – so that journalists are taught not to give any value judgements."

"What, not say if they think an artist is good or not?" Peggy lit a cigarette.

"Well, because they are all basically variations of the same idea, choosing between one or the other is like choosing between say, different flavours of Italian ice cream."

"That's a hint, isn't it? Which flavour would you like?"

"Strawberry. You are very kind. I'm afraid many of the articles I read in the art press are written in a language so obscure as to attract only the elite few, who are, of course, the powerful opinion formers."

"Like I was once," and she handed him a bowl of ice cream. "If you were alive, Herbert, you would write sensible things."

"Thank you. You're too kind. Peggy, there is something else that's different now. Governments, these days, want high museum attendance and particularly want to attract the lower classes."

"Oh yes, now I understand. Bring in the pickled sharks, the entertainment!" She was laughing. "I can see it all now, Herbert, why would any artist want to be truly avant garde when being conceptual is the road to riches and official recognition?" She continued, "Herbert, one thing I don't understand. If critics don't make value judgements about artists or works of art, how does the consensus decide what is good art?"

"Money."

"What?"

"High auction price means that a work of art is good; it gives it significance, as Jeff Koons said the other day."

"Hey, you know Papa, you are right. I read in a Sothebys

magazine, they're still sending them to me – where is it? Beside my bed here, 'the best art is the most expensive because the market is so smart'. What the hell do you make of that!?"

"Yes, well that's the way it is now. It is because aesthetic and monetary value are both subjective, that they are decided by auction prices."

"And that's objective?"

"I fear not, dear Peggy, but bid up by certain interested people. It raises the value of all the works they own by that particular artist."

He continued: "The artist has become 'a brand' due to this celebrity thing, and he, or of course, she, is promoted through a big powerful 'branded' gallery. And it isn't necessarily the work of art itself, it is the context in which the work of art has been placed which adds to its value."

"Context? What the hell is that?"

"If it is in a top collection it is more valuable."

"Like mine for instance! Ha, ha. Herbert, this conceptual art, it is designed to appeal to a mass culture, isn't it?"

"Indeed. And it does. To a mass global culture. Attendance at museums, there are a lot of nearly identical museums in every capital city around the world these days, is right up."

"People like conceptual art, do they?"

"I am sure many do."

"But it misses one ingredient, doesn't it?"

"Mmn, delicious ice cream. What are you thinking of, Peggy?"

"Emotion."

Herbert looked at her, teaspoon of ice cream in mid air.

"Maybe," she continued, "lots of people are entertained, but are they moved? Herbert, art, for me, must be convincing. And it does come down to the character of the person making it, and maybe that is why I spent my life getting to know these artists so well."

Peggy's eyes were sparkling: "For me, Herbert, art should be emotional. Someone in a newspaper put it well the other day. Let me find the Sunday Times. She put on her glasses. "Ah, here we are, by someone called A A Gill,[1] whoever he is: "I want art to transcend me, to move me, to be inspiring, to depress, excite, manipulate, realise feelings, and thoughts which are too subtle and deep to put names on. I want it to make me laugh or make me feel'...Herbert, I'll just say, 'sexy', but he says something else."

"Well put! I have to say I agree. And, Peggy dear, I fear the public assume because an artist is exhibited in a museum that he must be good. And when they are not moved, they assume it must be they who are not intelligent enough to understand it."

"But, they are not dumb, just hungering for emotional content!"

"So, are you saying that there could be an disenfranchised mass of people for whom art is not catering, Peggy?"

"Could be, huh?" said Peggy, cuddling a small fluffy dog.

"By the way, Peggy, there is an artist, called, er, let me see, yes, here we are, Tracey Emin. Thought you might like her work. So I've brought a catalogue to show you."

"Don't tell me she uses readymades!"

"I am afraid so; her Turner Prize piece is called, *My Bed*."

"Let me read it." Peggy put her glasses on again. "Her life is her art, yes, yes, oh, and she has had abortions. I think I have had nine abortions, you know, Herbert."

She continued reading, "and one work is called *Everyone I have ever slept with*. Ha ha."

She put down the catalogue and took off her glasses. "Everyone I have ever slept with – Herbert, how many is that? People say I've had a thousand lovers. But that's ridiculous! But I admit I had so many in New York I can't remember their names." Peggy was laughing, but she looked vulnerable.

"I was needing love." Peggy's large eyes filled with tears. "Everyone I ever truly loved, my father, my sister Benita, my first real love John, my daughter Pegeen, they all died when they were young. Then Max left me, but I don't think he ever loved me. This piece by Tracey Emin reminds me of Frida Kahlo. It is emotional, confessional, and I love it."

"Well, I have to hand it to you, Peggy, you're still, as Alfred Barr would say, seeing art."

"I'm in the *zeitgeist*, aren't I?" Peggy smiled. "Now, Herbert, please, how do we get out of this 'ism'? Especially as it seems we are not training artists to be able to make art in any other way."

Then she added: "And, by the way, I read the other day that Picasso, despite everything that's been happening in the contemporary art world, is still Britain's favourite modern artist!"

"Still a job for you there then, Peggy," and Herbert laughed. Then he became serious: "But, we must remember, there isn't a law of progress, but of reaction."

"So reaction against Duchamp? About time. He would approve."

"In art, Peggy, a movement, like conceptualism, once established, normally deteriorates as it goes on. It achieves perfection with a burst of energy. But then there is the melancholy certainty of a decline."

Herbert was still very serious. "Great revolutionary leaders, like Leonardo, Picasso and Duchamp are men with a single and simple idea and it is the very persistence with which they pursue this idea that endows it with power."

"I can't see art ever going back to its traditional role of imitating nature, can it?" asked Peggy.

"No, I can't either. But what we have now are shifts in style leading to dead ends...."

"Peggy!" Herbert leaned forward and looked Peggy straight in the eye: "I believe the whole of art needs rethinking."

"Wow! How do you mean?"

" We are divided between fields of activity, science from

philosophy, technology from science, and science from art. The result is an inability to understand the totality of this world. To relate emotion and material things."

"Really?"

"In this divided world, art has an open brief. Taken negatively it leads to dead ends and triviality. But taken as a challenge it could forge a new and expanded concept of art bridging fields of knowledge and linking our intuition and our intellect, chaos and order."

"That's so beautiful, Herbert." Peggy walked over to the window and looked out. Although late in the afternoon, it was still sunny so she put on her outrageous sunglasses. "Hey, there's Nicholas Serota." Peggy waved furiously out of the window.

"Good, he's coming up," she said. "Let's ask him his thoughts on this, and about the Tate and these young artists. The Tate had a role, didn't you say, Herbert, through the Turner Prize, of bringing them establishment endorsement?"

"But you know, Peggy, when you think about it, it's not so different from your day, when you were the big collector, supporting and promoting artists and working closely with Alfred at MoMA."

Just then a middle aged, tallish man with short greyish hair and glasses appeared at the door.

"Sir Nicholas, or may I call you Nick?" said Peggy holding out her hand. "Do you know Sir Herbert Read?"

"Hi, my name is Hans Ulrich Obrist," said the man.

"Oh, you are not.... we thought.... oh dear.... are you here for the Biennale?"

"Yes, I'm a curator. I do shows with Matthew Barney, Jeff Koons and...."

"We've been thinking about the art world." Peggy interrupted. "Art is terrible now, isn't it? Where is it going from here?"

"Well, I think the 21st century will be more about the polyphony of centres."

"What does he mean, Herbert?"

"I'm not exactly sure, but I think he means the linking of art from different countries around the world."

"I'm interested in non-mediated work," said Obrist.

"Herbert, what does he mean?"

"I assume he means performances and videos, as that grotesque Matthey Barney, who intruded earlier, makes."

"Object-led art can also rewarding."

"What the hell is object-led art?"

"I think he means paintings and sculpture and installation."

"There are lots of ways art can travel," said Obrist. "Through an object, through a quasi-object and through a non-object."

"Really?" said Peggy, trying to understand.

"It is easiest in some ways because an object is an object and the object will always be the object, but the object..."

"Really?" Peggy was confused.

"As Jeff Koons says," Obrist continued, "the object communicates the information you want the viewer to have a dialogue with. The art takes place within the viewer – they are what's important."

"Ah! Just like Marcel said!" said Peggy.

"Very nice meeting you, Miss Guggenheim, and you too, Sir Herbert. I have to say I had thought you were both dead."

"Peggy, I must go, too" said Herbert. "Thank you for a lovely lunch."

"'Till our next lunch – and the next 'ism," said Peggy, as she saw her guests out.

"Medici or maneater, which am I?" thought Peggy and she looked out of the window. "Hey, isn't that Glenn Lowry? He'll tell me what's been going on at MoMA." She waved furiously, "Glenn, up here..."

* * *

We talked about Herbert Read's thoughts about art and the direction it could go towards. Leonardo agreed with Herbert Read's analysis because, of course, he is the prime example of an artist who understood the totality of this world and combined science and art.

Leonardo seemed more philosophical and reflective as the afternoon wore on. He had been, it seemed to me, wounded by many things in life and at one stage said despairingly, "While I thought I was learning how to live: I had been learning how to die."

I wanted to comfort this beautiful man and so I reminded him of his greatness, and how posterity has confirmed him as the supreme universal genius; but he looked mournfully at me and said: "The greater one is the greater grows one's capacity for suffering."

* * *

Notes

[1]AA Gill in the Sunday Times, September 2009.

We had some refreshments and Leonardo cheered up.
I was about to tell him about another world entirely.

Act VII

The Players

Damien Hirst (b.1965) studied at Goldsmith's College of Art. He is a prominent member of the Young British Arts Group, which dominated the London art scene during the 1990s. He won the Turner Prize in 1995.

Tracey Emin RA (b.1963) was born to a Turkish father and English mother in Margate, Kent, and then studied at the Royal College of Art. She was nominated for the Turner Prize in 1999 and represented Britain at the Venice Biennale in 2007.

Paul Goldfarb is an entirely fictitious art collector. His words are an amalgam of four or five real-life art collectors.

Jeff Koons (b.1955) trained at art school in Baltimore and worked as a Wall Street broker before becoming an artist.He has achieved world record auction prices for works by a living artist. He had a major show at the Serpentine Gallery, London in 2009.

Takashi Murakami (b.1963) studied traditional Japanese art and has a doctorate in Nihonga, a mixture of Western and Eastern styles. He works with digital and commercial media, using themes from popular culture.

Tracey Emin's flat, London, September 2008

Tracey Emin is lying on a double bed, wearing high heeled platform shoes. She is drawing, and listening to Blur. She hears the buzzer and leans over to answer it. A short stocky man, in his early forties, walks in.

"Damien, you're a star," she said as he threw bags of crisps on the bed and brought in bottles of beer and a Tesco carrier bag.

"Here you are, Trace,' he said in his Leeds accent. He opened a beer and handed it to her.

"You just caught me doing my drawings for my next show at Jay's." She showed Damien the one she was doing.

He looked at it; then turned it upside down. "Looks like a frog wearing shoes."

"It's me masturbating. Oi, don't sit on my bed. It is a work of art. It's a seminal piece."

"I can see that," he said and laughed, and sat on a filthy armchair beside the bed.

"It's been exhibited in the Tate, been in the Turner Prize

and so I've got to keep it just like this. Used condoms just like this, dirty knickers just like that."

The more Damien looked at it, the more unpleasant the bed looked; empty cigarette packets, empty beer bottles, slept-in sheets.

"And I've sold it! I've got loads of money." She pulled out a wad of notes. "Do you like my new artwork?" And she fanned out the notes between her long, brown legs.

"Ha ha, how about you, Damien? Hey, I was nearly forgetting, how was your Sotheby's sale today?"

"Made a hundred and eleven million....pounds."

"Fucking hell!" And Tracey's face erupted into its wide crooked smile, and then she laughed raucously for a good few minutes.

Suddenly Damien was animated, and he looked at her. "Yeah, Trace, it was magic. This proves that art is more important than money. 'Cos Lehman Brothers fucked up today, and the punters still bought my art."

"Cheers. Open another beer, Dame. We're celebrating." Tracey's accent was fashionable estuary, fitting for a successful artist in turn of the millennium Britain. "Since I did my bit on the telly, pissed, everyone's been buying my art like hot cakes. We're both celebrities."

Damien got out another couple of beers, opened them and giving one to Tracey said, "You know, Trace, the art world is very shallow and very small and it's very easy to get to the top of it. Then, where the fuck do you go? You've got to constantly reinvent yourself."

Damien got up from the chair and stood alarmingly close to the gleaming white toilet on the other side of Tracey's bed.

"Don't you use that! It's a work of art. It's by my friend Sarah, and Paul Goldfarb is coming in a minute to buy it. So don't you pee in it."

"Excuse me!" he said, and sat down again. "Yeah, 111 million pounds. Art is about life, and the art world's about money. And I'm the only one who fucking knows that. Everyone lies to themselves to make it seem like it's the other way. But it isn't, Trace."

"You and I, Dame, we've both come a long way. My family were poor, from Margate. Dad was gone; he had lost his money."

"Leeds. We had no money either, Trace."

"My Mum loved my brother and me, strange to think we were an accident."

"My Dad left when I was twelve."

"I was raped. Pass us a Wotsit, I'm starving."

He threw over a few Wotsits from the bag he was eating from. "Always wanted to be a famous artist."

"Did you? I was disillusioned with life."

"The only thing I had in life was what I believed, and I built everything on that."

"I knew there was something better, there was an outside, an outside of me, and that somewhere wasn't Margate." Tracey was inspecting her face in a hand mirror.

"Loved all that abstract expressionist art at Leeds Art School. De Kooning, Pollock. And Patrick Heron. Colour. I'm a fucking colourist. I am the fucking Matisse of colour."

"That's why you do your spots, don't you? Your spots are lovely," and Tracey smiled her crooked smile.

"Yeah, all my colour goes into spots, they're fucking brilliant. But at Leeds, they said art went to pot after 1960. And I agreed."

"What, like from Warhol? Open us another beer. Where's Paul? We'll get him to take us out for dinner. I wanna wear my Vivienne Westwood. Shows my tits off nicely. I'll get a photo in ES magazine. It's good for business, as

Andy would say. Ha, ha."

Damien picked up another beer. "Yeah, from Warhol. They said it went to pot after 1960, and I agreed. They taught us all this abstract stuff. And I was doing all this Schwitters collage stuff on cornflake packets." Damien made curtain motions with his arms.

"Sounds like curtain designs." Tracey was applying mascara.

"Yeah. I realised what I had done was all shit." He opened the beer and handed it to her.

Then he said: "Drawing and painting I'm not so good at. It was going nowhere and I was going nowhere."

"Well, I left art for a while, part of my emotional suicide. I attempted to give up everything that I loved that did not love me back." Tracey's eyes welled with tears and her newly applied mascara smudged.

"I trashed it all up and swept it all up into a heap, like this," and Damien swept up some rubbish into a heap with Tracey's kitchen broom.

"Yeah sorry, this flat's a fucking mess. But I call it home."

"And that heap of rubbish, Trace, that was my first year show at Goldsmiths."

"Yeah, just like me. I'd spent three years out of art school struggling to make something beautiful only to arrive at the tearful conclusion that I would never be a great artist."

"I had this massive fear. Felt I'd failed." Damien downed the rest of the bottle of beer in one go.

"My life was too important to chop it up into little pieces in an attempt to make art. That was why I had always failed." Tracey wiped the smudged mascara with an old tissue she found on the bed.

Damien opened another beer. "Then I realised that art hadn't lost it. I came round to this art I hadn't liked. This new art, art we'd seen at the Tate, art since the 60s, since Warhol."

Damien stood up and raised his voice: "Art is about life, Tracey. It's up there it's not on the ground."

"Yeah, me too. I began to rebuild myself, using the experience of failure as my foundation." Tracey was applying pink lipstick.

"I wanted to make an artwork about something, about something important."

"Otherwise you'd be a fucking curtain designer. Ha ha."

"Yeah, I wanted to make important paintings to change people's lives. So…,"and Damien swept the floor a bit more.

"It was about sweeping it all….."

"What do you mean, 'it'? Life?"

"Yeah, life, up in a pile. And that was it! What if, what if, what if….What if I had a life cycle in a box? And what if I had a rotting fucking cow's head? And it was a real head and it had flies on it and…."

"How's that? I'm looking beautiful now." Tracey put down the mirror and showed off her face to Damien.

"Nice, Trace. It was the best piece I've ever made."

"Didn't you go and see that Koons show at Saatchi's around that time?"

"Yeah. It was ace, massive. Our tutors said it was recycled Warhol and no good." Damien raised his voice: "Then I thought 'fucking hell, everything's shit in the art world. What we are doing here at Goldsmith's is definitely better.' Trace, we had to navigate the existing art market or there was no hope."

Tracey was still inspecting her face.

"But you know, Trace, when I was doing my fly piece everyone laughed their fucking heads off and said, 'You've lost your fucking head, it's shit.'"

"But they've always laughed at new masterpieces. Like

they did at that big painting by Picasso of those prostitutes."

Tracey was looking at Damien's Tesco bag. "I'm getting peckish." Then she said, "Saatchi bought that fly piece, didn't he?"

"Yeah and I got, 'You cunt. You're just selling out. How can you do that morally?' And I was thinking, 'I've fucked up'. But I'm not Charles Saatchi's barrel organ monkey."

Damien offered Tracey a Wotsit. "Then when it was showing at the Saatchi gallery, Bacon came to see it, and so did Lucian Freud."

Buzz

"That's Paul Goldfarb," said Tracey, and she got up to open the door.

"Tracey, my dear," and Paul and Tracey kissed on both cheeks. Then he turned to Damien, "well done mate."

"Yeah, thanks."

"How much?" asked Paul.

"111 million... pounds."

"Paul, you could take us out tonight, we're celebrating." said Tracey. She took Paul's bottle of champagne, opened it and poured three glasses. Paul was a youngish man of middle height and the beginnings of baldness. He was wearing an

Armani light coloured suit and was inspecting the sofa to see if he could bear to sit down.

Tracey pointed to Sarah's 'toilet'. "Here you are, Paul."

All three of them inspected the toilet. "Have you got some details about it, Tracey?" asked Paul.

"Yeah, let me read them to you: It says Sarah Lucas; *The Great Flood*; 1996; plumbed toilet, cigarette butt; Exhibited at the The Institute of Contemporary Art, 1997."

"Nice provenance. Does Sarah say anything about it anywhere?"

"Let me see, she says: 'I'm saying nothing. Just look at it and think what you like.'"

"I suppose if the right people in the art world say it's a great work of art then I suppose it is," said Paul and he removed some empty orangina bottles from the sofa and sat down.

"Yeah. They do," said Tracey.

"Life is art," said Damien. "Duchamp didn't quite do it but putting a fucking toilet into a gallery is fantastic."

"The problem is," said Paul, "I was bought up a Kantian – to believe that art is sacred and has a beauty which is absolute and universal..."

Tracey was getting fearful Paul wasn't going to buy it, "it works," she interrupted. "Pull the chain."

"...and that it contains mysterious principles," continued Paul.

"Pull the fucking chain," Damien said.

Paul pulled the chain, and mouthed, "Wow."

Damien, in a put-on camp voice said, "It's transforming the ordinary into the extraordinary."

"Sarah's an artist like we are, and she chose this as a work of art, just like Duchamp said," said Tracey.

"So am I to believe that an artist is a superior spirit endowed with special gifts who can distinguish between what is and what is not art?" asked Paul.

"Yeah," said Tracey, sipping her champagne.

"Well, I buy what I like. But it must have visual appeal and the public must respond to it as I show works in my private museum."

"Actually," said Tracey, "you're lucky you're even being offered it; there's a waiting list for Sarah's works."

"Come on, Paul, buy it," said Damien. "Great art is when you walk round the corner and go fuckin' hell what's that. And they're gonna say that when they see this."

"Is this great art? Come on, Damien, great works of art don't just arise. They are made, not just by the artist, but by the dealers, the curators, the critics and by us the collectors who support the work."

"Yeah, I suppose it's sort of like a collective belief emerges." said Tracey.

"For an artist," Damien was pacing the room now, "if you sell you're great, if you don't, you're shit."

"That's true. Validation of market price overshadows everything." said Paul. "I'll check her auction records and let you know tomorrow."

Damien sat down and ran his hands through his hair. "You know, Paul, you are right, is it great art?" He was silent for a minute, then he said: "I had a big dance with conceptual art; but there are things in art which are dead end. Conceptual art, abstraction, they're total dead ends."

Tracey and Paul looked at each other.

"I've always had a romance with painting." He stood up again. "Painting is dead! Long live painting! That's what I'm going to do now. Rembrandt! Bacon! Everything I've done has been leading up to this."

There was silence.

Then Tracey said, "well, you always tear up the rule books, Dame."

Then a few moments later she said: "Here Paul, my latest work of art, drawn with my own fair hands," and Tracey handed him a drawing.

"What is it?" Paul turned it upside down. "Looks like a frog wearing shoes."

"It's me masturbating, for my next show at White Cube."

"OK, here you are," and Paul handed her a wad of notes.

She kissed him on the forehead, "thanks Paul, you're a star."

"Well, I've got eight hundred Warhols. Got Koons. One hundred and fifty of yours, Damien, and now I've got some Traceys. I don't buy just to put on walls. I'm a market maker."

"It's good you keep prices up, Paul," said Tracey.

"Yes, I bid on you today, Damien, kept your prices up. I have to, to keep the value of all my works by you up."

"Hey, listen, you guys," Tracey interrupted, " I've just had a text from Elton. We're seeing him later tonight and I've got to think of a line of poetry for my blanket I'm making for him."

"You're the artist, Tracey, the special person with the creative skills," said Paul. "I'm just an ordinary hedge funder."

Paul was looking around the flat but recoiled when he saw the dirt and mess everywhere. "My friends from Chelsea can't believe I come to the East End to places like this. But I want to find the next great artist I can buy into. The next Warhol. I think it's you, Damien. And then, of course, I'll be looking for the next one after you to buy into."

"I don't think I am the best artist who ever lived, but I've discovered a lot on the way I can pass on to the artists behind me on the same journey," said Damien.

"That art is the best business, like Warhol said," said Tracey and she laughed her raucous laugh.

"I like Andy Warhol," said Damien. "Honest fucking geezer. You've got to walk in there and go, 'I'm shit and proud of it'. You win. That's Warhol."

Damien had cheered up, "It's any great artist. It's Bacon. Shit and proud of it. And, you know what, not just proud of it, prepared to die for it."

"If you look in the history books," said Paul, "every other artist than Pollock, Judd, Warhol, and you Damien, and I am sure you too now Tracey, will be just a footnote."

"Picasso and Pollock – they're both egomaniacs. The fucking great ones. They never failed artistically. And basically that's what it takes – it's like fuck everything you hear. Carry on with what you believe. It's fantastic and it works."

"I know what you mean, Dame," said Tracey, combing her shoulder length brown hair. "When I really want something I make it up. Like it's all I've thought about, dreamt of, craved and believed. And then it has become a reality." And then she added, "and you don't have to be born with balls to have balls."

Damien's mobile rang.

"Jeff, babe. Yeah thanks. 111 million...no, pounds. Yeah, mate; high value, high significance." Damien did the thumbs up sign to Paul and Tracey.

Paul was speaking quietly to Tracey, "Koons iconizes suburban banality brilliantly. I own several."

"Can't hear; be quiet you two," said Damien. "What mate? Your new show at the Serpentine. Yes? Your..." and Damien put on an American accent....

"..... personal iconography. You've been in a dialogue with Andy and Duchamp. You have Elvis, you end up with the Mona Lisa and LQOOQ."

"She has a hot ass. I know that one!" shouted Tracey.

"What's this, Jeff?" Damien said, "Mona Lisa's lips updated for a modern, commercial age? Fucking brilliant."

"Thanks, bye mate, see you," and Damien turned off his mobile.

"So, where were we?" said Paul. "Yes, the great artist. He, or she, is a genius."

"And has balls," said Tracey, as she refilled the glasses.

" Michelangelo, Leonardo, sure they were geniuses from day one." said Damien taking a gulp of champagne.

"But I don't believe in genius. I believe that artists are normal people who manage to harness what is important for everybody. Everything I experience I transform it into a universal truth that will be meaningful to people if I put it in a global fucking fashion."

Tracey had a sip of champagne, "there is spunk and there is mental spunk and it's the latter that gets me up in the morning, that makes me change my life, that moves the world."

"Art's about living now," said Damien.

"And the fragility of existence?" asked Paul.

"Where's God now?" Damien started shouting: "God's fucked off. So all those big issues like art and science and death are all clambering about on this barren landscape where

God used to exist."

"I always think, just replace the word love with God and the world will be a better place," said Tracey.

"That's beautiful, Tracey," said Paul. "Well, you've got works in the Tate now, Damien.

"I'm not Nicholas Serota's barrel-organ monkey either," shouted Damien who was getting drunk. "Museums are for dead artists. Thirty years from now the Tate can have the best of the bunch – tried and tested by posterity. I want to make art on my terms...

"...and," he added, "you can bullshit people who are alive now but you can't bullshit people who haven't been born."

"True. But for me, owning art is exciting, fun and sexy," said Paul.

"Art for me is like a lover," said Tracey. "Hey, is that a good slogan for Elton's blanket?"

" Sounds good," said Paul. "Owning art for me, is to enjoy the work everyday, the ego trip of possession, the look what I've got factor, and making the personal aesthetic decision which defines you within the entire context of art history."

Damien put on a posh voice: "A good buy, picking something ineffable."

"Heck, the money does matter," said Paul. "No one wants to pick a loser, and, if it goes up in value it reminds you that your choice was smart one, you picked a winner, even if you don't want to sell, the picture looks a lot better when someone offers you ten times the price you paid. Where's the....?" Paul asked Tracey.

"Don't know how clean it is, but through that door there."

While Paul was out of the room, Damien urinated in the Sarah Lucas toilet.

Tracey was still giggling as Paul came in again. Paul continued where he left off: "If you can buy something at £60,000 and sell it for £600,000 two years later, everyone wants in. That's what's been fuelling the market. Making it that much more sexy."

"The money aspect of the work is part of life – it becomes a commodity and manages to stay art," said Damien. "I find that really exciting."

"Kiss me, kiss me, cover my body in love. Would Elton like that?" asked Tracey.

"Try it on him," said Damien. "I'm involved with now, and now is different from any other time. Money is an element in the composition and if it becomes king then it just does."

"Oo, I could just fancy a Burger King to keep me going before we go out to dinner," said Tracey. "Damien, what's in your Tesco bag there?"

"I've got...this." And he brought out a skull encrusted with diamonds.

"Oh no, not that again," said Paul. "I've already made you a good offer on that."

"How much is it?" asked Tracey.

"It's fifty......fifty million....er pounds, that is." Damien was suddenly unsure of himself. "Look, everything in the whole world is worth what anyone else is prepared to pay for it. And that's it. Simple."

"Well your shark has been called the Mona Lisa of today, so maybe your diamond skull will be too," said Tracey. "There Paul, you should buy it. The icon of the 21st century."

"Listen Paul, which makes the most amount of money – the Mona Lisa or the T shirts, the earrings, the mugs, the post cards, the souvenir pens? Trace, if someone said to you, you have a choice, I'll give you the actual Mona Lisa or the merchandising rights. What would you take? In terms of art what would you take, Tracey?"

Damien was pacing the room again. "It's like if you've

got the Mona Lisa on your wall, all you'd get is people coming in your house and going: "Fuck off. Is it fuck!". Know what I mean? Nothing against the artist – it's been kicked up its own arse, the Mona Lisa. It's destroyed. It's been destroyed as an image."

"Is that what Duchamp was saying when he painted a moustache on it?" asked Tracey.

"Yeah," said Damien, and his mobile rang.

"No, I don't want double glazing. Paul, see if you can work out what this geezer is saying."

Paul took the mobile and listened for a while. "Murakami!" Then he mouthed: "'Takashi Murakami'. Yes, I will pass on your congratulations. 111 million, I think, no.... pounds. Yes, I think he is pleased. I love your work, by the way. Yes, I know, superflat. I'm on the waiting list for one. Yes, your Oval Buddha? Yes, what's that word? Can't quite catch it. Yes, yes, validated, ah, got it, by your show at MOCA. I know you are a Warhol fan. Your operation makes Warhol's look like a lemonade stand!"

Tracey was inspecting her Vivienne Westwood dress for stains.

"What's that? Your Louis Vuitton work is what?" Paul

was still trying to understand Murakami. "Your urinal? Yes, oh I see, changing the context of an object. Yes, I see, the Louis Vuitton boutique is a readymade. We've actually just been talking to Jeff, that's a coincidence. He was saying how he's moved on from criticising capitalism to celebrating capitalism. You know what, Murakami? Your art *is* capitalism."

"My diamond skull – *it* is art as capitalism, capitalism as art." Damien was talking to himself. "It's the icon of now, of the 21st century."

Damien went over to his mobile phone in Paul's hand and switched it off while Paul was in mid conversation. "Paul, fucking buy it. 50 million pounds will make it the Mona Lisa of the 21st century."

"OK, so I'm thinking about it," said Paul. "But, 50 million pounds is an end of history, triumph of capitalism price. And I don't suppose it even includes the merchandising rights."

Then he shook his head. "This art, it's creating value out of.... nothing! For whom? For a breed of new super-rich collectors. Mugs, like me. We're looking for tokens of glamour and prestige; and this art, this art delivers back to us images of our own greed and emptiness."

Damien and Tracey were silent.

Paul's mobile phone rang: "Hello. What! What do you mean? All? Because of Lehman Brothers. Thanks very much, mate. I'm ruined." He turned off his mobile.

Damien and Tracey sat not saying a word.

"No, Damien, I can't buy your skull. So it isn't being sold for 50 million pounds; so it isn't the Mona Lisa of the 21st century.   What did Koons say? High value means high significance. So, no value means no significance."

"Tracey, Paul Goldfarb is not taking us out to dinner," said Damien.

* * *

Leonardo felt very much for these two young artists and told me how he had been born illegitimate. He told me how he had gone through a period of crisis when he left the studio where he had been apprenticed. He felt he had been called to a high mission, but he had no money to meet the challenge, sometimes not even enough to buy paints.

He told me about his relationships with a long list of patrons which were always, it seemed, troubled and turbulent. Like both Picasso and Duchamp, and also increasingly like Hirst, he did not want to be beholden to anyone. Leonardo hated having a patron, but he needed one to pay for his household.

I was worried that Leonardo would be upset by Damien Hirst's comments that the merchandising rights of the Mona Lisa could be more desirable than the painting itself. But once again, I was struck by Leonardo's good sense. He knew that the popularity of Mona Lisa merchandise is because of the timeless significance of the painting itself. While he spoke we both looked over at Mona Lisa's enigmatic smile.

I asked him about the concept of artists as celebrities. He was very relaxed about it. He said that all the established artists of the time including himself, Michelangelo and Raphael, were famous in their home towns and amongst the powerful men of Italy and even further afield.

Leonardo was of course a scientist as well as an artist. When I mentioned Damien Hirst's piece which incorporated flies, he told me how he had imprisoned flies so that he could study the variations in their buzzing.

He was fond of morals and throughout my narrative he told me many which related to the story, all reiterating man's ignorance of natural laws of the universe.

I began to find out that Leonardo had a personality which ranged through fun, wonder and delight at the world to utter despair at man's egotism and wickedness.

* * *

Later the same day

Act VIII

Leonardo da Vinci's studio.
Florence, c. 1507

We had been together for seven hours in Leonardo's studio; with me recounting this 'Divine Comedy', the story of the 20th century art world; and our 'Virgil' sometimes smiling, sometimes laughing out loud. Sometimes he looked disillusioned and shook his head.

Leonardo and I agreed that virtually all of life was contained in this story: Creativity, love, sex, kindness, goodness, selfishness, disrespect, greed, power, comedy, money and death.

Salai meanwhile, had been lounging around for most of the day; sometimes drawing, sometimes strumming his lute quietly, or sometimes parading in yet another pair of shoes.

It was time to think about the big question. The question I had come to seek Leonardo's guidance on.

"So, Leonardo (he had said that I might call him by his name), that is the story of modern art. From cubism to now, by which I mean 21st century now. We have witnessed the important moments. The key players have played themselves and spoken with their actual words.

"But," and I turned from Leonardo to an imaginary audience, "as two of the most powerful men in the art world: Marcel Duchamp and Hans Ulrich Obrist[1], have said, 'Just as important as the artist, is the viewer. The artist performs one part of the creative process, the viewer completes it. Art takes place within the viewer.'

"You then, members of the audience, when you look at a work of art, you are the viewer; you decide if it is a work of art for you. And you, the viewer decide posterity, not the artist."

And so, as you can see, dear reader, *your* opinion too is important. Please think about the big question: Where can art go from here, and who will be the next modern master?

Your opinion is needed to help define the art of the future.

After my emotional speech, I turned back to Leonardo: "Leonardo, you are our guide. What do you think?"

Leonardo sat me down in front of him.

It seemed an eternity, but at last he spoke:

"The soul..." he said.

Then he looked into my eyes. "The eye is the window of the soul. Through the eye, the artist explores the mystery of the laws of the universe."

He stroked his beard, and continued: "The soul is content to stay imprisoned in the human body because, thanks to our eyes, we can see these things; for through the eyes all the various things of nature are represented to the soul."

"The soul..." He was so wise. "The eye, the soul and the..."

"Una cosa mentale."

"The mind. Art is a mental act. Is it then, the tension between the three; the eye, the soul and the mind, which produces great art?" Leonardo could instinctively see that these three elements had got out of balance.

"So, when the emphasis is on the idea or the mind, as it is in this 'ism, this 'ism of conceptualism..." (I was thinking aloud), "and the eye is purposefully excluded, the soul is excluded too?

"Yes!" We looked at each other for a few moments, then I said: "The soul. Emotion. Inner emotion. Isn't it just as Kandinsky was saying?"

He nodded.

"So, for fifty years we have been purposefully excluding the soul and emotion from art? "

He looked at me. He really was extraordinarily handsome.

"So, Leonardo, as Herbert Read said 'there is not a law of progress but of reaction.' So, maybe, the soul and emotion will once more take their proper place?"

"Oh mortals, open your eyes. We..." he was speaking slowly, "must understand and interpret the mysterious laws of the universe."

"Yes, that is the role of the artist!"

But now something else was worrying me: "Money!" I turned to my imaginary audience again: "Does money corrupt art?"

I was thinking aloud about the words we had heard that day: "'Don't deal in this money society. Preserve your freedom.

Without that no worthwhile contribution is ever made.'

"This, may I remind you, members of the audience (and you too, dear reader), was said by Duchamp, the very father of conceptualism; conceptualism which has, in turn, fostered an art world ruled by money!"

Another thought came to me, and now I spoke both to Leonardo and to my imaginary audience: "Maybe it is because this art leaves out two essential elements of the trio, the eye and thus the soul keeping only the mind in function, that it encourages a monetary evaluation of art?

"And Leonardo, what was it that Herbert Read also said? 'When art is separated from other fields of life...'",

"Science?" suggested Leonardo.

"Yes, science, for example," and I continued Herbert's words: 'man becomes unable to relate emotion and material things....'"

"What else did he say? 'If art has no confines, and is taken negatively, it leads to the dead ends and triviality of much recent art.' And that was the conclusion even of our young conceptual artist Damien Hirst!

"Herbert also said: 'This open brief, taken as a challenge, could forge a new understanding... of the totality of the world!'

"And," I added, "it is possible that we are moving to a new *zeitgeist*." I told Leonardo about the seismic changes the 21st century world is experiencing: "We have economic meltdown, we are concerned about climate change and we have, yet again, renewed political instability."

"Maybe," I suggested, "these profound issues will take over from the *zeitgeist* of shallow mass popular culture, characteristic of the post-modernism of the last fifty years. "For that feeds, it seems, only on itself, reinventing itself as a parody, rather than exploring..."

"The mysterious laws of the universe." Leonardo finished my sentence.

Just then I remembered the words of another genius: "Albert Einstein said 'art is a profound thought expressed in the simplest of ways.' Leonardo, that's what I personally, as a viewer, look for in a work of art. But," and I turned once again to my imaginary audience: "Other viewers may agree or disagree with me."

"But who," I asked him, "will be the next modern master? Someone who has that,that ....?"

" Burning desire?" he suggested.

"Like you.... which an artist must have, to understand

and interpret this universe. But one who is in tune with the *zeitgeist* and who uses, perhaps, all the modern technology available in the 21st century, as I am sure, Leonardo, you would do. But his, or her art, has also to understand the totality of the world, stretch boundaries and yet be timeless. And he must use his mind and....." and we both said it together and laughed...

"Eyes."

"In other words, a genius, like you." I said, and leaned over and kissed him.

"Thank you, dear Leonardo, for your wise advice."

I picked up my handbag and discovered that I was missing my mobile phone, my iPod and my purse.

Leonardo said he thought it must be Salai and that he had stolen from him too, in the past. "I cannot get him to confess, although I am certain he is guilty," Leonardo told me.

Leonardo called to Salai: "Little unclean one," (this was one of Leonardo's nicknames for Salai), and told him to return them to me (he must have been stealing something every time I went to the toilet).

Leonardo was fascinated by my 21st century gadgetry and asked me to explain it to him, which I am afraid I could not. He was thrilled when I gave him my iPod as a thank you present; and immediately put in the ear pieces and started listening to Blur.

I looked for a while at Leonardo's wonderful portrait of me. Then I took a last long look at *Mona Lisa*, that still unsurpassed masterpiece. I thanked him for allowing me to seek his guidance on this important question, so relevant to us all.

I thanked Salai too, for everything. I opened the door, walked down the stairs, opened the heavy front door, walked down the street lined with tall houses and back to the café on the corner.

Notes:

[1]Duchamp has been described by many artists as the most influential artist of the second half of the 20th century. Hans Ulrich Obrist was voted by *Art Review* as the most powerful man in the art world in 2009.

Selected Bibliography

Benhamou-Huet, Judith. *The Worth of Art (2)*. New York: Assouline Publishing, 2008.

Behrman, S.N. *Duveen: The Story of the Most Spectacular Art Dealer of All Time*. New York: The Little Book Room, 2002.

Blast to Freeze: British Art in the 20th Century. Ostfildern-Ruit, Germany: Hatje Cantz Publishers, 2002.

Buck, Louis and Judith Greer. *Owning Art: The Contemporary Art Collector's Handbook*. London: Cultureshock Media Ltd, 2006.

Buck, Louisa. *Moving Targets 2: A User's guide to British Art Now*. London: Tate Gallery Publishing Limited, 2000.

Burn, Gordon and Damien Hirst. *On the Way to Work*. London: Faber and Faber,

Carey, John. *What Good Are The Arts?* London: Faber and Faber, 2005.

Collings, Matthew. *It Hurts: New York art from Warhol to now*. London: 21 Publishing, 1998.

Collings, Matthew. *Blimey! From Bohemia to Britpop: The London Artworld from Francis Bacon to Damien Hirst*. Cambridge: 21 Publishing, 1997.

Emin, Tracey. *Strangeland*. London: Hodder and Stoughton, 2005.

Friedman, B.H. *Jackson Pollock: Energy made visible*.

Guggenheim, Peggy. *Confessions of An Art Addict:* Ecco Press, 1997

Hackett, Pat. *The Andy Warhol Diaries*. New York: Warner Books Inc, 1989.

Hamlyn, Paul. *The Life and Times of Leonardo*. London: The Hamlyn Publishing Group Ltd, 1967.

Hirst, Damien. *The Cancer Chronicles*. London: otherCRITERIA, 2003.

Hirst, Damien. *Pictures from the Saatchi Gallery*. London: Booth-Clibborn Editions, 2001.

Holzwath, Hans Werner. *Jeff Koons:* Taschen, 2000

Hughes, Robert. *Nothing If Not Critical: Selected Essays on Art and Artists*. London: Collins Harvill, 1990.

Jones, Alan and Laura de Coppet. *The Art Dealers: The Powers Behind the Scene*

Talk about the Business of Art. New York: Clarkson N. Potter, 1984.

Kahnweiler, Daniel-Henry with Cremieux, Francis. *My Galleries and Painters.* London: Thames and Hudson Ltd, 1971.

Lindemann, Adam. *Collecting Contemporary.* London: Taschen.

McCully, Marilyn. *Loving Picasso: The Private Journal of Fernande Olivier.*

Muir, Gregor. *Lucky Kunst: The Rise and Fall of Young British Art.* London: Aurum Press Limited, 2009.

Obrist, Hans Ulrich. *A Brief History of Curating:* JRP/Ringier & Les Presses du Reel, 2009

Potter, Jeremy. *An Oral Biography of Jackson Pollock.*

Read, Herbert. *A Concise History of Modern Painting.* London: World of Art, 1959.

Richardson, John. *A Life of Picasso:* Jonathan Cape, 1996

Richter, Irma A. *The Notebooks of Leonardo da Vinci.* New York: Oxford University Press, 1952.

Samuels, Ernest. Bernard Berenson: *The Making of a Legend.* London: The Belknap Press of Harvard University Press, 1987.

Sassoon, Donald. *Leonardo and the Mona Lisa Story: The History of a Painting Told in Pictures.* London: Overlook Duckworth, 2006.

Scully, Sean. *Resistance and Persistance Selected Writings.* London: Merrell Publishers Limited, 2006.

Spurling, Hilary. *The Unknown Matisse.* London: Hamish Hamilton, 1998.

Stallabrass, Julian. *Art Incorporated: The Story of Contemporary Art.* New York: Oxford University Press, 2004.

Stallabrass, Julian. *HighArtLite: The Rise and Fall of Young British Art.* London: Verso, 1999.

Stein, Gertrude. *The Autobiography of Alice B. Toklas.* London: Penguin Books, 1933.

Sylvester, David. *Francis Bacon:* Pantheon, 1975

Tacou-Rumney, Laurence. *Peggy Guggenheim.* Paris: Flammarion, 1996.

Taylor, Brandon. *Art Today.* London: Lawrence King Publishing, 2005.

The Andy Warhol Museum. *13 Most Beautiful...Songs for Andy Warhol's Screen Tests*. London: Plexi Productions, 2009.

Thompson, Don. *The $12 Million Stuffed Shark: The Curious Economics of Contemporary Art and Auction Houses*. London: Aurum Press Limited, 2008.

Thornton, Sarah. *Seven Days in the Art World*. London: Granta Books, 2008.

Tomkins, Calvin. *Off the Wall: Robert Rauschenberg and the Art World of Our Time*. New York: The Penguin Group, 1980.

Tomkins, Calvin. *The World of Marcel Duchamp*. New York: Time-Life Books, 1996.

Tomkins, Calvin. *Post- to Neo-: The Art World of the 1980s*. New York: Henry Holt and Company Inc., 1988.

Vollard, Ambroise. *Recollections of a Picture Dealer:* Constable, 1936

Walker, John A. *Art and Celebrity*. London: Pluto Press, 2003.

Warhol, Andy. *The Philosophy of Andy Warhol (From A to B and Back Again)*. London: Harcourt, Inc, 1975

Weld, Jacqueline B. *Peggy, The Wayward Guggenheim*. Penguin Books.

Werner Holzwarth, Hans. *Jeff Koons*. New York: Tachen, 2009.

Wright, Karen. *"Hans Ulrich Obrist: Art for All."* Now. 26 September 2009, London.

Credited Images

Front cover: Mona Lisa background, The Louvre and Bridgeman Art Library
Photograph of Caroline Wiseman, Brian Usher

Acknowledgements

To everyone who has helped enable this book to be published at break neck speed, including Jennifer Ball, Maggie Butcher, John Hale-White and Janet Treloar. Particular thanks to Kirsten Rich for lending me her copy of *The Da Vinci Code;* Professor Amee Carmines for enlightening me about Dante's *Divine Comedy*, and my partner, Francis Carnwath, for his forbearance when the house was full of books.